The Making of the NAE

THE FIRST 25 YEARS

By Lee Edson

Edited by Marlene R. B. Beaudin

NATIONAL ACADEMY OF ENGINEERING
1989

Acknowledgments

The time and effort of a great many people have gone into the preparation of this book. The author and editor wish to thank all who contributed to its production. Our special thanks go to NAE Home Secretary Alexander H. Flax and staff editor H. Dale Langford who spent many hours resolving the endless questions of substance, syntax, and context. We also wish to thank the staff of the NAS archives and especially its director, David J. E. Saumweber, and archivist Janice F. Goldblum for the hours spent verifying the document's details. To Pamela Reznick who designed the book and who was responsible for the book's production and to administrative assistant Kimberly F. H. Garcia who provided invaluable assistance in manuscript production, we are most grateful.

We thank Bruce S. Old and Hugh H. Miller who, seeing the value of a history such as this, had begun the collection of materials which they willingly shared with us. We also acknowledge the assistance of Howard J. Lewis and William C. Salmon who oversaw and guided early administrative and creative aspects of the project.

At various stages throughout the preparation of the book, a number of people provided interviews, reviewed chapters, or provided comments on the work as a whole: Richard Anthes, Jesse H. Ausubel, Stephen D. Bechtel, Jr., Riley M. Chung, Walker L. Cisler, JoAnn C. Clayton, John S. Coleman, S. Douglas Cornell, Thomas B. Deen, Gerald P. Dinneen, James D. Ebert, Thomas E. Everhart, Martin Goland, John V. N. Granger, Jerrier A. Haddad, N. Bruce Hannay, Allan R. Hoffman, J. Herbert Holloman, John D. Holmfeld, William G. Howard, Jr., Edward R. Kane, Raphael G. Kasper, Ralph Landau, Howard J. Lewis, Harold Liebowitz, Clarence H. Linder, Thomas L. Martin, Jr., Norman Metzger, Hugh H. Miller, James H. Mulligan, Jr., Bruce S. Old, Courtland D. Perkins, John S. Perry, Don I. Phillips, Kerstin B. Pollack, Frank Press, James B. Quinn, Simon Ramo, Robert C. Seamans, Jr., Frederick Seitz, Chauncey Starr, H. Guyford Stever, Myron F. Uman, Eric A. Walker, John F. Welch, Jr., and Robert M. White.

We also thank the other members of the NAE staff who provided research, read drafts, prepared manuscripts, and performed the many duties necessary for completion of this book: Barbara J. Bishop, Bruce R. Guile, Bette R. Janson, Maribeth Keitz, Carrie Levandoski, Belinda F. Smith, and Douglas L. Wolford. Finally, we wish to thank the colleagues, coworkers, and others whom we have not mentioned for their assistance, patience, and encouragement in this endeavor.

Lee Edson
Marlene R. B. Beaudin

Preface

This book is a brief account of the origins and the first twenty-five years of existence of the National Academy of Engineering (NAE). It is in no sense a formal history, much less a complete one. Rather, it records the principal imperatives, themes, and objectives that brought the Academy into being and the events and people that cast it into its present form and role. Much of the story is told through the recollections of Academy officers, councillors, members, and staff who took part in particularly significant events and activities that influenced the evolution of the Academy structure and defined its role on the national and international scenes.

The twenty-five years since the founding of the NAE has been a period during which the central importance of engineering and technology for the economic progress, general welfare, and the quality of life grew ever more evident to governments in all nations. During this period, the NAE has emerged as a principal focus of engineering leadership at the national level, drawing into its membership ranks outstanding engineers from the entire range of engineering activities in industry, academia, government, and other sectors of society. The engineering leadership of the NAE has come to play a major role, in parallel with the primarily academic and scientific leadership of the National Academy of Sciences (NAS), and in concert with the medical leadership of the Institute of Medicine, in advising the federal government on the major scientific and technological issues of our age. This is exemplified by the jointly governed institutional mechanisms of what has come to be known as the Academy complex, of which the National Research Council (NRC) is the central and largest component.

The story of the NAE as it unfolds in this book is thus as much an account of the evolving relationships among science, engineering, governments, and the public as it is a record of the building of the NAE as an institution capable of playing increasingly important roles in those relationships, national and international. The major program activities reported are not only those carried out by the NAE independently but also those of particular engineering interest and importance in the Academy complex, especially for the more recent years since the NAE assumed its present role as full partner with the NAS in the NRC and most other activities of the complex.

In a work of this sort, only the highlights of the many diverse circumstances, events, and people that contributed to the origins and twenty-five-year development of the Academy can be included. The selection of these highlights was inevitably a matter of judgment. The people and events cited in this book are at best a representative cross section of all that contributed to the making of the Academy as we know it today.

The author and editors wish to express their gratitude to the many NAE members and staff and others in the Academy complex who assisted them by providing documents and personal recollections. Without their assistance, a work of this kind could not have been written. Equally, they wish to express their apologies to the many individuals whose important activities and contributions to the work of the NAE and its institutional development could not be included or may not have been given as much weight as they might have warranted. Finally, although extensive efforts were made to ensure the accuracy of the statements made and the reports of events in this book by consulting with many of the people involved, cross-checking the documentary record, and having the manuscript independently reviewed, the author and editors take full responsibility for any inaccuracies that may remain.

Alexander H. Flax
Home Secretary, National Academy of Engineering

Contents

Engineering and the Growth of America

CHAPTER I

Engineering and the Growth of America

n 1961, shortly after leaving office, President Dwight D. Eisenhower attended a dinner ceremony at the Statler Hilton in Washington, D.C., a celebration unlike any he had ever experienced. Eisenhower, the center of the celebration, was there to receive a unique medal, not for his accomplishments as president or his prowess as the commander of the Allied forces, but rather for his leadership in conducting one of the world's greatest engineering projects, the organization and management of a technological and military structure that resulted in the victory in Europe in World War II.

For almost two decades since the end of the war, the public perception had been that World War II was mainly a "scientists' war." Although engineering achievements were vital in making the A-bomb possible, the credit, nonetheless, went to J. Robert Oppenheimer and his team of physicists. Although electrical engineering talent and advances in design and manufacture put radar into operation, radar was always talked of as one of the physicists' great achievements. And, though engineering triumphs led to shortcuts in manufacturing, improvements in machines, and production of the nation's fleet of gallant Liberty ships and the vast armadas of aircraft, it was the scientists' achievements that were spotlighted.

The reasons for the public's inability to sort engineers from scientists were understandable. The dire necessities and reordered priorities of war had blurred the boundaries between engineering and science as projects were rapidly advanced from basic research to production. As the nation adapted its human resources to meet the massive wartime needs for technical expertise, many of the physicists and other scientists were functioning much of the time as development engineers. Under these circumstances the image of engineers and engineering had been obscured.

The decision to honor Eisenhower with the 1960 Hoover Medal—an engineering medal awarded jointly by four engineering societies* to such giants of engineering as Vannevar Bush and Charles Kettering, as well as to President Herbert Hoover himself—signaled the recognition by leading engineers of the monumental dimensions of the engineering feats that made victory possible in World War II. As Brig. Gen. S. L. A. Marshall put it in his eloquent address on the occasion:

> To dig the Panama Canal and free it of rock slides over many years required the movement of 72,306,000 tons of earth. . . . To operate the European Theatre through one year of war on the continent and to stage invasion from the United Kingdom entailed the movement of 73,737,680 long tons, most of it transported across oceans and narrow seas amid peril . . . [and] . . . two artificial harbors, the Mulberries, which were to facilitate across the beach movement of freight until a port could be won . . . . Mulberry A, at Omaha Beach, was to avail a harbor of two square miles with moorings for 19 ships.

When the engineers left the dinner that night, they felt pride in the achievements of their profession. But another three years would pass before that pride would manifest itself in the founding of the National Academy of Engineering (NAE), election to which would become one of the profession's highest recognitions for the accomplishments of engineers.

Engineers had not always felt a need for greater public recognition. For perhaps a hundred years—roughly between 1850 and World War II—

*American Society of Civil Engineers; American Institute of Mining, Metallurgical, and Petroleum Engineers, Inc.; American Society of Mechanical Engineers; and Institute of Electrical and Electronics Engineers

engineers enjoyed a solid public reputation that was tantamount to hero worship. The opening of harbors, the building of canals and bridges, and the joining of the great railways across America put the engineer in this enviable position of public acceptance, even admiration. Eric A. Walker (president of NAE 1966–1970) once noted that in the early history of the Republic almost anything engineers had to do to harness nature was regarded as good.

The eruption of the Civil War underlined the importance of engineering to the government. President Abraham Lincoln was said to have been so fearful of an invasion by the Confederate Navy that, according to one biographer, he continually looked out the White House window toward the Potomac River, half expecting to see a fleet of Confederate ironclads—each beaked with a two-ton iron wedge—steaming for the capital. Even though he was told the *Merrimack*, symbol of technological progress in the Confederate Navy, could not navigate the shallow Potomac, his concerns led him to go outside the military to engage the services of Charles Ellet, a renowned civil engineer in private practice. Ellet believed in, and eventually sold the Union forces on, the virtues of battering rams in naval warfare. It was the use of the ram in the famous battle between the *Monitor* and the *Merrimack*—a battle that was actually fought to a draw—that is credited with destroying the fearsome image of the Confederate fleet and helping to bring naval victory to the North.

Formation of the National Academy of Sciences

In 1863 Lincoln took an important step on behalf of science and engineering when he signed into law a bill establishing the National Academy of Sciences (NAS) under federal charter to provide help and advice to the government. Its main provision stated that "whenever called upon by any department of the government [the Academy] shall investigate, examine, experiment and report upon any subject of science or art [i.e., technology]."

Frank B. Jewett, president of NAS from 1939 to 1947 and a member of the NAS's engineering section from the time of its creation in 1919, noted somewhat grandiloquently: "It [the NAS charter] is one of the most sweeping delegations of power coupled with obligations of service to the Nation which the sovereign authority has ever made to a group of citizens completely outside the control of political government. In less than forty words, the

The battle between the Union *Monitor* (left) and the Confederate *Merrimack* (right) on March 9, 1862, the first battle between ironclads.

The founders of the National Academy of Sciences portrayed with President Lincoln at the signing of the Academy charter. *Left to right:* Benjamin Peirce, Alexander D. Bache, Joseph Henry, Louis Agassiz, President Lincoln, Senator Henry Wilson, Admiral Charles H. Davis, and Benjamin A. Gould. Painting by Albert Herter.

Act of Incorporation in effect created in the whole domain of science a Supreme Court of final advice beyond which there was no higher authority in the Nation and ensured that so far as was humanly possible its findings would be wholly in the public interest uninfluenced by any elements of personal, economic, or political force."

The concept of the Academy was the brainchild of six American scientists and engineers who got together in an interesting way. Professor Alexander D. Bache, grandson of Benjamin Franklin and head of the U.S. Coast and Geodetic Survey, conceived the idea of a centralized government commission on science in 1851 and brought it to the attention of his friends Joseph Henry, head of the Smithsonian Institution, and Admiral Charles H. Davis, chief of the Bureau of Navigation. Apparently Davis seized on the idea, believing that, among other things, the Navy could use such an organization to sort and evaluate the suggestions it was receiving for weapons of war. He submitted a proposal to Navy Secretary Gideon Welles, who promptly created the Permanent Commission of the Navy Department, with Henry, Bache, and Davis as charter members.

It was Davis who soon saw in this commission the potential for a greater impact on the advancement of American science, comparable to the impact of the contemporary academies in Europe. He enlisted the support of Louis Agassiz (whose son, Alexander, was later elected president of NAS from 1901 to 1907) and Benjamin Peirce, both of Harvard University, and

Benjamin A. Gould of the Dudley Astronomical Observatory at Albany, who agreed that it was important to establish an academy that would raise the standard of American science.

Five of the six scientists and engineers (Henry was not present) met on February 19, 1863, at the home of Senator Henry Wilson of Massachusetts and drafted the bill that would incorporate the Academy. Wilson introduced the bill on the Senate floor the next day. It was passed by voice vote in both houses on the last day of business and signed into law by President Lincoln on March 3, 1863. Bache was elected the Academy's first president at an organizational meeting in April.

As things turned out, the fledgling National Academy of Sciences (it had fifty members, twenty percent of whom were engineers) was not a major factor in the Civil War. However, it was not entirely idle. The Navy called on the Academy to advise on the prevention of corrosion on the bottoms of the iron ships in the fleet. It also asked for advice on protecting ships' magnetic compasses against deviations caused by the iron hulls and for an evaluation of the charts then being used in navigation. The Academy was again called on in the spring of 1864 to investigate a boiler explosion aboard a newly launched gunboat—an explosion that had killed twenty-eight members of the crew—and to determine whether structural defects were responsible. The Academy submitted a report, with recommendations that were incorporated into the future design of boilers.

After the Civil War, Henry, who succeeded Bache as president in 1867, expanded the Academy's role from exclusive government service to include the encouragement of original scientific research. In 1872 the membership was enlarged to seventy-five, and restrictions were set on the number of new members that could be elected within any year. In 1878, in his last address to the Academy as its president, Henry cautioned: "Great care must be exercised in the selection of members. It must not be forgotten for a moment that the basis for selection is actual scientific labor in the way of original research, that is, in making positive additions to the sum of human knowledge—connected with unimpeachable moral character." Such an exhortation helped set the standards of membership and also served to establish the Academy as an elite organization.

The Golden Era of Engineering

During the same period, engineering grew in power and prestige as a profession, and its accomplishments were widely hailed in the popular press. Indeed, for the next forty years, one engineering triumph followed another and was duly recorded. Transportation, communication, materials, structures, and power each produced its hero engineers. No wonder engineer-industrialist Sam Florman, a prolific writer on the engineering profession, saluted the 1865–1905 period in the United States as "the golden era of engineering."

During this time, each engineering breakthrough was attended by a celebration comparable to a coronation. When the first telegraph cable was laid from America to Europe, 25,000 people paraded the streets of New York for sixteen hours. At the moment on May 10, 1869, when the Union Pacific and the Central Pacific railways were joined into the first transcontinental line at Promontory Point, Utah, Americans across the land rang bells, fired cannon, and lit bonfires. Three thousand people gathered at the Great Salt Lake to see the last tie placed and the last spikes driven—one each of gold, silver, and iron—to complete the great enterprise. Even as late as 1937 the opening of the Golden Gate Bridge was celebrated by a fiesta attended by

Opening day for the Golden Gate Bridge, May 28, 1937. With a main span of 4,200 feet, it was then the longest suspension bridge in the world.

The Panama Canal, completed in 1914,
includes three sets of double locks,
each 1,000 feet long, 110 feet wide, and
70 feet deep.

200,000 people and was followed by a week of pageants, parades, and other festivities.

International exhibitions were even more popular. In 1851, six million people—the equivalent of about one-quarter of the U.S. population—visited the Crystal Palace in Hyde Park, London, to wonder at the triumphs of mechanical engineering. Philadelphia's 1876 Centennial Exhibition—the first successful World's Fair in America—attracted crowds to such marvels of mechanical ingenuity as the typewriter, the continuous-web printing press, the first Corliss engine, the telephone, and the refrigerated railway car. During the 1889 Paris Exhibition, Alexandre-Gustave Eiffel's great edifice—a tower 1,000 feet high with a lacy framework of iron—drew two million paying visitors, and it remains one of the world's great engineering attractions.

Perhaps the most spectacular achievement in that era of the great engineer-builders was the construction of the Panama Canal, a ten-year project that linked the Atlantic and Pacific oceans, becoming the greatest artificial waterway in the world. Completed in 1914, the project was one of the largest and most difficult ever undertaken, requiring not only the labor of some 43,000 men who moved more than seventy-two million tons of earth, but also the conquest of yellow fever and malaria. The army engineer in charge, Lt. Col. (later Maj. Gen.) George W. Goethals, was lionized wherever he went.

Scientists and Engineers in Service to the Nation

A key figure in the promotion of U.S. science and engineering and the potential of the National Academy of Sciences and later the National Research Council was astrophysicist George E. Hale, director of the Mt. Wilson Solar Observatory and the youngest member of the Academy when elected in 1902 at the age of thirty-three. As NAS foreign secretary (1910–1921), Hale made a detailed study of European academies, observing how scientists cooperated with their governments and with their own organizations and concluding that the U.S. Academy was accomplishing only a fraction of what it could be doing for science in the United States.

This conclusion may have surprised many because the sciences had advanced substantially in the United States since the early days of the century. Unlike the first half of the nineteenth century, when mechanical inventions had dominated, the second half showed how scientific research and discovery could lead to useful applications and indeed to entire industries. The telegraph, for example, was the product of fundamental discoveries in physics, and mining was advanced by basic work in geology.

With the arrival of World War I came renewed interest in the sciences and a move in the technical communities to search for a way to mobilize the nation's technical resources. Once again engineers took the lead. In 1915, under the joint leadership of the Secretary of the Navy and America's premier inventor, Thomas A. Edison, engineers from the engineering societies joined with industrialists to establish the Naval Consulting Board—a body designed to muster engineering talent whenever it might be needed in

George E. Hale, chairman of the National Research Council from 1916 to 1919, with the spectroheliograph and the Foucault pendulum in the Great Hall of the Academy building, 1925.

William H. Welch

John J. Carty

Gano Dunn

the military effort.

In the spring of 1916, as war raged in Europe, Hale, NAS President William H. Welch (1913–1917), NAS Vice President Charles D. Walcott, and a small committee called upon President Woodrow Wilson to request official support for the establishment of a national research council to enable the scientists and engineers to place their expertise at the service of their country should the United States enter the war. In anticipation, Hale had been working to establish a strong relationship between the engineering societies, their industrial supporters, and the NAS. As originally conceived, the council would include representation from all branches of fundamental and applied sciences under the protection of the Academy charter; it would thus be a powerful instrument in advancing all fields of science and engineering.

Unfortunately, the Wilson White House was slow to accept the Academy's plan. It was an election year, and Wilson was seeking a second term on a platform of keeping the United States out of war. Although events were shaping America's decision, Wilson at the time did not want to support a proposal that suggested he was privately preparing for war while publicly advocating strict neutrality. He met with the committee at the White House but stopped short of agreeing to their plan.

Hale and his colleagues—physicist Robert A. Millikan, Gen. John J. Carty, and Gano Dunn, president of J. G. White Engineering Corporation— were so annoyed with the president's rebuff that they briefly considered drafting a statement for use by the managers of a Republican campaign being mounted against Wilson. General Carty discussed this tactic with Col. Edward M. House, the president's aide, who immediately telephoned the president. The result was that on July 24, 1916, only three months after Wilson had turned down the first proposal, he sent Welch a letter approving the preliminary plan for the National Research Council and also sent a confirming wire to Hale, who promptly informed Dunn.

The National Research Council (NRC) was formally organized in the fall of 1916 with Hale as chairman and Walcott and Dunn as vice chairmen. Presidential appointments came from the armed services and several other government agencies; the remaining members came from industry and universities and were appointed by the NAS after consultation with the presidents of leading scientific and engineering societies. Dunn, who was also president of the United Engineering Societies and chairman of the Engineering Foundation, generously provided Hale with office space in New York and the entire income of the foundation for a year (approximately $13,000).

Millikan, who was later to win a Nobel Prize for his work on electrons, became the NRC's first full-time research director. His first major project was to develop techniques for detecting and destroying enemy submarines that were then wreaking havoc on Allied shipping. Through his strong interest in antisubmarine warfare, Millikan made major contributions to the war and was influential in encouraging the establishment of an antisubmarine station at New London, Connecticut.

In 1917 Welch resigned as president of NAS, and the membership elected Vice President Walcott to the presidency. A man preeminent in science within the federal government and the scientific community as a whole, Walcott was a strong supporter of Hale and his efforts on behalf of the National Research Council.

In May 1918, in view of the NRC's accomplishments, Wilson issued an executive order authorizing the continuation of the NRC on a peacetime basis. Thus was created the first U.S. organization to support the broad interaction of science, engineering, education, and industry in advisory service to the government on a permanent basis.

Robert A. Millikan

A man of considerable energy and boundless ideas, Hale proved an influential advocate for engineering in the institution. Citing the success of the NRC engineering division during the war and noting the dearth of engineering members in the NAS when compared with its counterparts in Europe, Hale proposed a deliberate buildup of engineering in the NAS.

Yet, when a separate engineering section of NAS membership was established in 1919, only one member of the original section on physics and engineering chose to join the engineers; the rest stayed with physics (the physics and engineering section had been disestablished in 1915, after which there was no section on engineering, only physics). However, Frederick Seitz (president of the NAS from 1962 to 1969) in reflecting on the history of that era noted that a number of the members who remained in the physics section were actually "red-blooded engineers."

In all, the new section had only nine original members. Gano Dunn, elected to membership in 1919, served as acting chairman. This section gave explicit recognition to engineering as a distinct and important part of the NAS; however, the subsequent lag in the engineering section's growth was ultimately to become an important factor in the establishment of the National Academy of Engineering.

Engineering in the National Research Council

The fact that engineering had been the most active division in the NRC following World War I helped cement the relationship of the NRC to the engineering profession. However, the next two decades saw a considerable reduction in national engineering projects as the military industrial establishment of World War I was dismantled and the Great Depression settled in.

Once the NRC became a permanent advisory institution, Hale, Dunn, Walcott, and others set up a committee and worked to secure funding for a building. Millikan personally raised a substantial share of the $185,000 required to purchase a site. Carnegie Corporation of New York contributed $5.0 million, then a staggering sum, to the NAS for the purposes of the NRC. Ultimately, $1.35 million of the Carnegie gift was used for the construction of a building in Washington that would be appropriate to house the new NRC along with the Academy. In reviewing the grant request, Elihu Root, president of the Carnegie board noted, "the same power of science which has so amazingly increased the productive capacity of mankind during the past century will be applied again, and the prizes of industrial and commercial leadership will fall to the nation which organizes its scientific forces most effectively."

The building was completed in 1924 and dedicated by President Calvin Coolidge with a glowing tribute to Hale. Hale's involvement with the NRC was so complete that he even coauthored with historian James H. Breasted the inscription encircling the dome of the Great Hall:

> To science, pilot of industry, conqueror of disease, multiplier of the harvest, explorer of the universe, revealer of nature's laws, eternal guide to truth.

Although these phrases omitted direct reference to engineering, the Academy ceremoniously assigned an office in the new building to the Engineering Foundation in appreciation for its assistance in establishing the NRC.

The Academy building in Washington, D.C., circa 1940.

In 1938 the position of engineering in the NRC became more prominent with the establishment of an Industrial Research Institute. Organized under the auspices of the NRC Division of Engineering and Industrial Research, then chaired by Vannevar Bush, the institute studied problems relating to the organization of research for industrial uses—mainly manufacturing. The program proved successful and in 1945 became an independent nonprofit association that today works to coordinate the study of problems confronting managers of industrial research and development.

Vannevar Bush

The outbreak of World War II brought a sweeping change in engineering and science. Out of the laboratories, some of them hastily thrown together, came radical advances in weapons and military hardware, including such marvels as the A-bomb, radar, electronic countermeasures, sonar, homing torpedoes, guided missiles, rocket weapons, radar fire control, bombsights, proximity fuzes, amphibious vehicles, incendiaries, and flame throwers, as well as blood substitutes, antimalarials, insecticides, and more. No such sudden flood of new discoveries and new products had been seen before. The wartime experience in accelerating and expanding research and development to achieve urgent national objectives had a powerful impact on the public perception of technology and science as a new force in the growth of the country.

From an institutional point of view, these developments were all orchestrated by a new civilian agency, the National Defense Research Committee (NDRC), established in June 1940 and later absorbed into the Office of Scientific Research and Development (OSRD)—an organization said to be the greatest (and possibly the shortest-lived) applied research and development complex the world has ever known. During World War II, Vannevar Bush, like Hale in World War I, was the driving force in organizing U.S. science and engineering. Bush, an engineer acting at the request of President Franklin D. Roosevelt, organized the OSRD because Roosevelt believed that a new civilian agency, backed by the government and independent of the military, was needed to coordinate the nation's wartime research effort.

Frank B. Jewett

Even before the United States entered the war, Bush enlisted the support of Frank Jewett, then president of NAS, along with James B. Conant, president of Harvard; Karl T. Compton, president of the Massachusetts Institute of Technology; and Richard Tolman, dean of the graduate school at

Supplies for the Allied invasion go ashore at the U.S. Mulberry harbor at Omaha beach off Celleville, France, in December 1944.

the California Institute of Technology. Thus, two engineers, a chemist, and two physicists spearheaded the efforts that eventually led to the integration of the nation's scientific and advanced technology resources in World War II. Harvey Brooks of Harvard has noted that whereas in World War I scientists were organized largely under the military, in World War II they enjoyed a more independent status working in a civilian environment under NDRC and OSRD.

NAS and NRC served the war effort in areas such as personnel selection and training and in early consultations on the feasibility of nuclear weapons. Moreover, many of the leaders of NDRC and OSRD were NAS members. NRC committees worked on the potential of biological warfare, looked into the suitability of specialized clothing and other supplies for the Quartermaster Corps, carried out medical research, and orchestrated other projects throughout the course of the war. The NRC War Metallurgy Committee worked on a large variety of wartime metallurgical problems, including increasing metal production, developing substitutes for materials in short supply, and improving metal performance characteristics.

The fundamental role of science and engineering in gaining military victory highlighted the importance of a sustained alliance between government and the scientific and engineering communities. The form of this alliance was to be much debated in subsequent years. Meanwhile the National Academy of Sciences, representing the leadership of the nation's science and engineering enterprise, was to move closer to center stage in national affairs.

Birth of the National Academy of Engineering

CHAPTER II

Birth of the National Academy of Engineering

"**A**ny engineer who occupied a seat of power or influence [in the postwar 1940s and 50s] would have felt the riptide of change coursing through the profession," science writer John Lear noted in the 1960s. As president of the National Academy of Sciences, Detlev W. Bronk was more than most in a position to sense and evaluate the great changes that had occurred.

The Bronk Era at the National Academy of Sciences

Bronk became a powerful figure in the world of science. He firmly believed that his personal mission was to increase the influence of science in national affairs by forging links between the National Academy and the other science agencies, such as the National Science Foundation, that were burgeoning on the national scene. Well connected in Washington and other world capitals, he is best remembered as one who simultaneously wore many hats; at one time he was president of the Rockefeller Institute for Medical Research (later The Rockefeller University), The Johns Hopkins University, the National Academy of Sciences, and the American Association for the Advancement of Science, and chairman of the National Science Board of the National Science Foundation (NSF). A gifted promoter of the values of science, Bronk, in the twelve years that he served as Academy president (1950–1962), acted to put the Academy at the center of the network of scientific and engineering organizations that had sprung up in the wake of the war.

Although Bronk's career was established in physiology, he remembered his roots as an engineer. He had received his first degree in electrical engineering and while still in college had worked part-time as an assistant power engineer with the Philadelphia Electric Company. It was this background that helped him develop the instruments in physiology that gave him considerable recognition in the scientific community. He turned to physics and biology because, as he once put it, he had "observed that all forms of engineering were extensions of the human being's natural means of coping with the environment."

Bronk was one of those rare individuals who, without apparent effort, had made the leap from laboratory research to science management. During the war he headed a neurophysiological research group that discovered how oxygen is transported through the body and brain and worked out guidelines that helped pilots avoid anoxia, or oxygen starvation of the brain, during high-altitude flight.

Detlev W. Bronk

Before taking over the NAS presidency in 1950, Bronk had served for four years as chairman of the National Research Council. As Academy president, he sought to strengthen the representation of engineers in the NRC and to encourage the growth of new technologies. Recognizing that NRC was occupied predominantly with engineering and medical activities, Bronk met with the presidents of the engineering societies—there were fourteen that were then organized as the Engineers' Joint Conference (later changed to the Engineers' Joint Council, or EJC)—to discuss ways of focusing the nation's finest engineering talent through the work of the NRC.

Bronk was aware that the engineering section of the NAS was small—thirty-five members, some of whom were retired—and that something should be done to revitalize it. However, he opposed the formation of an independent academy of engineering—an idea then being espoused by a few prominent members of the Engineers' Joint Council—because of his stated belief that with the proliferation of science organizations after World War II, the academy concept had become an outmoded instrument for affecting public policy. On the other hand, like his successors in the NAS presidency, he was well aware of the unique strengths and protection of the original NAS charter. It was in fact under Bronk that the positions of president of the NAS and chairman of the NRC were permanently unified.

As an alternative to a separate academy, Bronk considered enlarging the engineering membership but was later persuaded to reject the idea in the face of the argument that, given the fact that there may be five to ten times as many engineers as scientists, adequate representation of the nation's engineers might open the floodgates and overwhelm the traditional balance among astronomers, mathematicians, physicists, chemists, and biologists in the NAS membership. Bronk's preservation of the status quo did not sit well with many engineers who felt isolated from the Academy of Sciences—a feeling that grew when in 1955 Bronk was appointed chairman of the National Science Board of NSF.

Engineering in the National Science Foundation

The concept of the NSF had been suggested in 1945 in *Science the Endless Frontier*, the report of a high-level advisory committee chaired by Vannevar Bush and charged with assessing the postwar needs of science in the United States. After a protracted legislative history, the agency was established as a part of the executive branch with the National Science Foundation Act of 1950. In signing the bill, President Harry S Truman stressed the importance to the United States of maintaining leadership in science. Unfortunately for the engineering community, the emphasis of the final legislation was on basic research in universities, not on applied research. This structure was based in part on a strong belief among legislators that support for engineering would naturally be provided by industry and government agencies with specific mission needs. However, in the early years of the NSF, some academic engineers felt they were being bypassed for grants within NSF and blamed Bronk, though a critic of the era noted that they might have just as easily, and perhaps appropriately, blamed Congress for establishing the NSF's limited franchise. In fact, Eric Walker, then dean of the College of Engineering and Architecture at Pennsylvania State University, had sought to testify before Congress on the merits of establishing a National Science and *Engineering* Foundation but was persuaded to drop his efforts by Bush, who suggested that it might be prudent to get one thing at a time out of government. Walker remembers Bush's argument as being, "We can get the name changed later."

Of course nothing of the sort happened, and university engineers continued to claim that engineering research was being shortchanged and

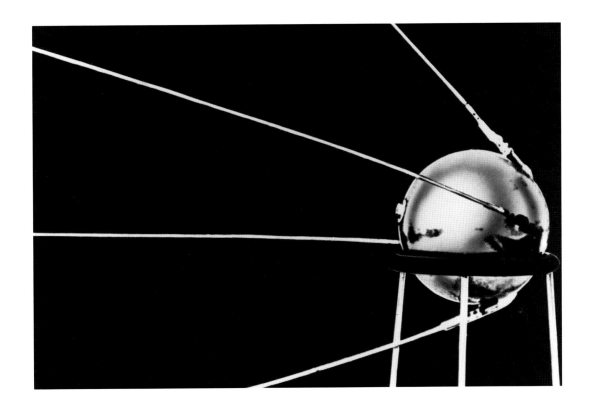

Sputnik I, the first research satellite launched during the International Geophysical Year (July 1957–December 1958). Weighing 183 pounds, it was launched on October 4, 1957, and measured temperature and pressure in an orbit ranging from 140 miles to 590 miles before returning to earth on January 4, 1958.

that they were being excluded from some of the early NSF projects. Members of the EJC continued privately to promote the establishment of an independent academy of engineering comparable to the NAS.

In 1956 Morrough (Mike) O'Brien, dean of engineering at the University of California, Berkeley, suggested to the president of the Engineers' Joint Council, Enoch Needles, that a national academy of engineering might be a good idea. Needles and Augustus B. Kinzel, vice president of research at Union Carbide and another prominent member of the EJC, subsequently went to Washington to discuss the subject with James Killian, science and technology adviser to President Eisenhower. Killian endorsed the concept of an academy but urged that it be formed in association with the NAS to avoid setting up two competing institutions.

No action followed, however, and the leadership of prominent engineering institutions continued to be dissatisfied with the status quo. Their dissatisfaction intensified in October 1957 when the Soviets launched *Sputnik I*, the first man-made object to orbit the earth. Now here was an engineering exploit of the highest rank occurring during the year-long, worldwide study of earth known as the International Geophysical Year (IGY), in which the

Soviet Union was a participant.

In the United States, IGY was a network of research projects orchestrated by an NRC committee and funded by NSF. The new *Vanguard* satellite program, announced in July 1955 by the Eisenhower administration, was to be part of the U.S. participation in the program. To meet the scientific objectives of IGY, the launch vehicle for *Vanguard* was to be developed and supplied by the Department of Defense through the Naval Research Laboratory, essentially independent of the large military missile rocket booster programs. After a failure of the launch vehicle in the *Vanguard* program in December 1957, some advocates of increased representation of engineering in NSF even speculated whether the launch of the first earth-orbiting satellite might have been accomplished here in the United States if the IGY project had been run by engineers instead of scientists. But the real issue was the restiveness felt by many research engineers. In 1958 Harold K. Work, associate dean of New

Three developers of the first successful U.S. satellite, *Explorer I,* show a model at a news conference in the Academy building, headquarters of the International Geophysical Year, January 31, 1958. *Left to right:* William H. Pickering, James A. Van Allen, and Wernher von Braun.

York University's College of Engineering and director of its research division, wrote

> We should accept the fact that the NSF is for scientists, and then try to set up a National Engineering Foundation to meet the need for basic engineering research. This should be supervised and operated by engineers and should fill the position that the National Institutes of Health do for medicine. This would seem to be a way to meet the basic needs of engineers while the NSF could continue to do the excellent job that it has done for scientists.

Harold K. Work

Work's suggestion did not produce an immediate reaction from the Eisenhower administration, but, a few months after he made it, he received an invitation to become director of the Engineering Foundation, an arm of the United Engineering Trustees in New York City. This venerable nonprofit organization had been formed in 1914 to advance engineering research with a $200,000 endowment from Ambrose Swasey, an engineer and head of a manufacturing company in Cleveland, Ohio. As part of its operation, the foundation had supported NRC's Division of Engineering with private funds until it became firmly established.

Engineering Seeks Greater Representation

In his new post as an advocate of engineering interests, Work worried about the future of his profession. In February 1960 Work ran across a summary in *Science* of a speech delivered during Engineers' Week by J. Herbert Hollomon, then general manager of the General Electric Engineering Laboratory in Schenectady, New York. Hollomon proclaimed that the time had arrived for engineers to look seriously at the proposal of setting up a national academy of engineering.

J. Herbert Hollomon   Antoine M. Gaudin

Impressed with this declaration, Work wasted no time in contacting Hollomon, and the two men agreed to merge their forces. The results of this association came to the ears of Kinzel, who, together with Work, prevailed on Antoine M. Gaudin, a professor at the Massachusetts Institute of Technology and chair of the Engineering Foundation's executive committee, to chair a feasibility study in the Engineering Foundation. Within a short time it became obvious to all involved that such a study would better be done in the EJC.

Fortunately for the future of engineering, Kinzel was then serving as president of the EJC as well as chairman of the Engineering and Industrial Research Division of the NRC, a post to which he had been appointed by Bronk. In July 1960 Kinzel wrote to Bronk informing him of the efforts underway in the EJC to investigate the establishment of an engineering academy. Kinzel then had no difficulty persuading the directors of the Engineering Foundation to give him a grant of $10,000 and the services of Work as executive secretary of an exploratory committee to study the requirements for the formation of an independent academy of engineering. In fact the foundation was to provide a total of $30,000 over the four years preceding the formal establishment of the NAE. An EJC study committee, formed under chairman Walter R. Hibbard, Jr., from the General Electric Research Laboratory, included representatives from the EJC, the Engineering Foundation, the Engineers Council for Professional Development and, at the invitation of the EJC, NAS President Bronk.

If the failure of past attempts to form an academy of engineering, including an ill-fated bill that had reached the floor of the U.S. Senate in 1917, came to mind, it did not trouble the committee. In November 1961, after much debate, the committee approved the concept of the new academy and proposed its structure.

Julius A. Stratton

At this point a new committee of EJC members was formed with Eric Walker as chairman to hammer out a constitution and move the engineering academy concept forward; but this was not easy, mainly because of opposition among the NAS membership. To overcome this reluctance, Walker asked Bronk to appoint a joint committee of engineers and scientists from NAS. Bronk decided instead to follow an EJC proposal to appoint a special NAS committee to work in tandem with a committee of the Engineers' Joint Council. The NAS committee was headed by NAS Vice President Julius A. Stratton, president of the Massachusetts Institute of Technology, while the EJC committee continued to be chaired by Walker. This time Kinzel moved over to serve as a member of the NAS committee.

The first meeting of the two committees was held on June 26, 1962, and foreshadowed things to come. Some members of the NAS committee believed that NAS had neglected engineers and should elect more of them to membership. The NAS leadership responded that enlarging the engineering section would not work and that it would not be practical to reorganize the NAS to accommodate the engineers. Clusters of opposition developed along familiar lines: engineers are too rich and powerful; they do not do enough original research; the military industrial complex for which many engineers labor will invade the NAS and affect the objectivity and credibility of its work.

Proponents of an increased role for engineering argued that the prestige accorded to engineers is equally well founded as that accorded to scientists, although it derives from different sources. Engineers, they pointed out, gain prestige in leadership in the application of science, scientists in fundamental discovery. Nevertheless, Walker assured proponents that, if formed, an engineering academy would primarily emphasize creative engineering contributions for membership.

Both sets of arguments were cogent, and the negotiations might have ended in stalemate were it not for the pervading influence of two extraordinarily perceptive men—Julius Stratton and Frederick Seitz. Although Stratton held degrees in physics and mathematics, he identified more closely with engineers and, as an NAS member, had chosen to be listed with the engineering section. During World War II he had done research at the famous Radiation Laboratory of the Massachusetts Institute of Technology and, after serving in a number of high positions, had become M.I.T.'s president.

Seitz, who had succeeded Bronk as president of the NAS in 1962, was a physicist. He had headed the physics departments in two institutions—Carnegie Institute of Technology and the University of Illinois—where physics was part of the engineering department. He also spent two years as a research physicist at General Electric Company and two years as director of the Manhattan Project's famous "Clinch College for Nuclear Knowledge," the educational and research facility on the Clinch River at Oak Ridge, Tennessee.

Frederick Seitz

Seitz confronted the problems of membership directly, turning his attention to the issue of balanced section representation in the NAS. He worried about the rapid shrinkage in the number of members who had M.D. rather than Ph.D. backgrounds in the life sciences as well as the decline in the number of engineers. In an attempt to remedy these problems, with the help of a committee chaired by NAS member Herbert E. Carter, professor and head of the Department of Chemistry and Chemical Engineering at the University of Illinois, and with the approval of the membership, Seitz introduced a quota system for election to the various broad classes into which sections representing related disciplines were grouped.

During this early part of his term, as Seitz recalls, neither he nor Stratton was in favor of an engineering academy as a method for remedying the engineering representation dilemma, although later both came to be firm supporters of an engineering academy. In fact Seitz recalls that as a member of the NAS Council before he became president, he had discussed the subject with Bronk on a number of occasions, but that Bronk was never won over to the concept of a separate academy.

For some time the arguments swirled not only between engineering and science but occasionally among the engineers themselves. According to Walker, one prominent engineer suggested that "the Engineers' Joint Council should be the vehicle to establish an academy of engineering and forget the NAS," but members of the Institute of Radio and Electrical Engineers (IREE), which was not represented in the EJC, objected, saying IREE would not support an academy unless it participated in its creation. Other objections were raised about the possible domination by the scientists. At times it seemed that the basic concept would never be realized because there were too many cooks stirring this particular broth.

The major problems were eventually ironed out, and in September 1962 Walker was able to submit to NAS a detailed prospectus from the EJC committee for a national academy of engineering. Not surprisingly, the prospectus was not immediately accepted. One of the basic questions was whether the NAS had the authority to include a new academy within its hundred-year-old congressional charter. Kinzel, with the backing of Walker and Killian, suggested that Seitz go to Capitol Hill and seek a new federal charter. Walker even threatened to get the engineers a congressional charter if Seitz did not.

But Seitz had no intention of going to Congress. He feared that such a move might end up in the rewriting of the original NAS charter. "No telling what you might get," Seitz said afterward. Instead he searched for alternatives and began to investigate the possibilities implied in the wording of the charter that gave the NAS the right to "make its own organization, including constitution, bylaws, rules and regulations." Why not expand the use of this clause to include a national academy of engineering, thus setting up an independent academy within the legal structure of the NAS? Seitz, assisted by his staff, spent many hours discussing the implications of using the charter—how could an engineering academy be given total autonomy when legal responsibility for whatever happened under that charter would still reside with the NAS?

Finally, they decided to test their concept on others. The idea appealed to Stratton, but he was not sure that the members of the NAS committee would go along with Seitz's proposal. He was convinced that he would have to invent a new means of overcoming the pockets of resistance and proposed a simple but appealing solution. Stratton suggested that any form of an academy of engineering accepted by the NAS membership be limited to a trial period of five years, after which its status within the NAS corporation would be reviewed. If, he added, the NAS wished to abandon the experiment after the trial period, it should arrange for a graceful exit of the academy. Kinzel wrote to Stratton that his suggestion was a "stroke of genius."

Birth of a New Academy

Negotiations were now coming to a close. In April 1963, Seitz wrote Walker that the NAS membership had agreed in principle to support the establishment of an engineering academy. A committee was to be appointed to arrange for the wording of a constitution, bylaws, and similar matters. In March 1964 Seitz appointed a Committee of Twenty-Five, a group that ultimately became the founding members of the National Academy of Engineering. The committee included ten members of the NAS engineering section and fifteen distinguished engineers who were not members of NAS; Augustus Kinzel was chairman.

When Seitz addressed the first meeting of the Committee of Twenty-Five in April, he laid out from the standpoint of the engineer the arguments for creating a national academy of engineering:

> 1. The rapid growth of science in the United States since World War I to a position of leadership in the world has apparently detracted somewhat from the image of the

engineer in the public mind after a long period in which the profession of engineering held a position of public esteem second to none. The establishment of a National Academy of Engineering could enhance the dignity and prestige of the engineering profession at this time and could redress the [im]balance.

2. The criteria for membership in the National Academy of Sciences, emphasizing creative scholarship as determined primarily through published research, place large and important groups of practicing engineers at a disadvantage. The new academy could, in principle, use broader terms of reference and include types of individuals who would not normally stand a good chance of being considered for membership in the engineering section of the NAS.

3. Many pressing problems involving technology on which the Government needs advice lie in provinces in which engineers are the primary experts. Advisory services on such problems might be handled more effectively if they were referred to a National Academy of Engineering rather than a National Academy of Sciences. Not only would the administrative leadership of a National Academy of Engineering be in a better position than that of the NAS to identify engineers for advisory services, but the engineers in the advisory committees might feel a higher level of professional status if their assignment were made through the NAE rather than the NAS.

Seitz continued by outlining his views on the ways in which the engineer serves society, mentioning innovation and invention, basic research, optimization of design, management, production, maintenance, standardization and controls, education, and technical sales. "The first great problem the founders of the new Academy will have to face," Seitz pointed out, "is that of deciding how to weigh these various categories when selecting its members." Seitz continued, "In general the National Academy of Sciences would give emphasis to basic research, innovation and invention, education and management, probably in that order. If the NAE adopts an essentially different pattern it must settle on these new standards in some way relatively early in its deliberations because of the great importance of the matter for the future composition and goals of the new Academy."

Seitz also expressed concern that if NAS and the engineering academy did not work closely together, the technical officers in the government agencies "will learn to play the two academies off against one another and thus undermine the effectiveness of both." Seitz thus laid out the philosophical framework of the National Academy of Engineering with the same care with which his predecessors had laid out the framework of the Academy of Sciences.

Although Seitz did not on this occasion address the question of how the engineering academy would gain its authority from the government, in October 1964 this question became the focus of debate by the Committee of Twenty-Five, with considerable airing of the conflict between those who wanted to draft an independent charter and those who wanted to make use of the NAS charter. It was at this point that Seitz presented his concept for establishment of the engineering academy under the NAS charter. Ultimately, the committee voted unanimously in favor of working within the NAS charter, but with the Stratton proviso that the arrangement would be reviewed in five years. On October 12, 1964, the NAS members at their autumn meeting, voted to "encourage the [NAS] President and Council to proceed with plans . . . for the establishment of a National Academy of Engineering under the Act of Incorporation of the National Academy of Sciences."

Only one step remained—approval by the NAS Council of the articles of organization of the National Academy of Engineering. This occurred on December 5, 1964, and the new Academy was born. Five days later the Committee of Twenty-Five elected Kinzel the Academy's first president. Eric Walker was named vice president, and Work became the first secretary.

In announcing the creation of the new Academy, the Committee of Twenty-Five confirmed the objectives and purposes of the institution:

■ To provide means of assessing the constantly changing needs of the nation and the technical resources that can and

Frederick Seitz and Augustus B. Kinzel announce the formation of the National Academy of Engineering at a press conference in December 1964.

Augustus B. Kinzel
NAE president, 1964–1966

should be applied to them; to sponsor programs aimed at meeting these needs; and to encourage such engineering research as may be advisable in the national interest.

■ To explore means for promoting cooperation in engineering in the United States and abroad, with a view to securing concentration on problems significant to society and encouraging research aimed at meeting them.

■ To advise the Congress and the executive branch of the government, whenever called upon by any department or agency thereof, on matters of national import pertinent to engineering.

■ To cooperate with the National Academy of Sciences on matters involving both science and engineering.

■ To serve the nation in other respects in connection with significant problems in engineering and technology.

■ To recognize in an appropriate manner outstanding contributions to the nation by leading engineers.

For the first five months of its existence, the National Academy of Engineering (along with the NRC Division of Engineering and Industrial Research) was located in New York City, operating out of the offices of the Engineering Foundation. In July 1965, Kinzel approached the Sloan Foundation for $500,000—$100,000 for initial operation of the NAE and $400,000 to be used to construct an auditorium to be added to the NAS building in Washington, D.C. Sloan approved the unrestricted $100,000 grant within the month, and in September 1965, NAE moved to Washington to share occupancy of the NAS building. In January 1968 the additional $400,000 was approved, and Sloan transmitted the funds to NAS through the NAE.

Kinzel served as NAE president less than two years (December 1964 to April 1966), dividing his time with the Salk Institute, where he had served as president and chief executive officer since 1965. During his tenure at NAE, Kinzel took every opportunity to promote the engineer's role as adviser to the government. Testifying before the House Subcommittee on Science

Research and Development in July 1965, Kinzel urged government to press the NSF to support engineering sciences, which had been neglected. Under direct questioning of the chairman, Emilio Q. Daddario, Kinzel indicated that he would like to see engineers at the top level of the NSF hierarchy, thereby laying the groundwork for future NAE presidents whose actions would lead to increasing engineering participation and representation in the NSF.

It was under Kinzel that the NAE adopted as its symbol a viaduct, or bridge, signifying the link between technology and science. After reviewing several proposed designs, the NAE Council settled on a design by George Tschemy on the staff of NAE member Elmer W. Engstrom, who was then president of RCA.

Symbol of the National Academy of Engineering

Kinzel worked hard to ensure that the NAE would be off to a good start. The government attention Kinzel was able to muster to NAE advisory potential had a "helpful effect on the morale of the engineering profession," he said. He listed areas of NAE's expertise as advice on the design of buildings to withstand earthquakes; environmental engineering; support of developing areas; and a program series for the Voice of America. In addition, he noted that NAE was working in cooperation with the NRC on ongoing activities such as patent policy, civil defense, emergency planning, and building research.

Leaving office on this optimistic note in 1966, Kinzel passed the reins to NAE Vice President Eric Walker, a British-born electrical engineer with industrial experience. Walker, a highly respected engineer, had worked hard to establish the Academy. For many years he had served as chairman of the Statutory Naval Research Advisory Committee as well as chairman of the NRC Committee on Undersea Warfare. Walker also had served as president of the American Society for Engineering Education and, during the Korean War, was secretary of the Research and Development Board in the Department of Defense.

At the time of his election, Walker was president of Pennsylvania State University and chairman of the National Science Board of the National Science Foundation. He took the helm as NAE entered the second half of the 1960s, one of the most turbulent periods in recent American history.

A Decade of Turmoil

CHAPTER III

A Decade of Turmoil

The latter half of the decade of the 1960s was a confusing and hectic period marked by, among other things, conflicting trends concerning the public perception of the profession of engineering. On the one hand, advances in the space effort enhanced the public image of engineers as people who could do almost anything, even put a man on the moon. On the other hand, engineers were increasingly blamed for the "technological ills" of society. In some eyes they were seen as insensitive in handling the problems of the environment, destructive in advancing military R&D, and insensitive to the public welfare in failing to exercise moral responsibility for the effects of their work.

As head of the new National Academy of Engineering, Walker was deeply concerned about these negative attitudes, even though he and his organization were not in a position to do much about their causes, at least at the start. One reason was the NAE's need to deal with the many organizational details required of the new Academy and to coordinate its pursuits with those of the NAS. The NAE had used the NAS's structure as a model of organization. One of its first moves had been to establish a governing Council with an executive committee to oversee the voluntary advisory committees that would perform the technical studies.

Walker also needed to confront NAE's funding and financial security concerns. The Sloan Foundation gift secured by Kinzel would not be sufficient to support any long-term Academy activity. In 1965 Kinzel had established the *ad hoc* Development Committee chaired by John W. Landis, manager of the atomic energy division at Babcock & Wilcox Company. The following year, Walker and the newly appointed chairman of the committee, Philip Sporn, chairman of the Systems Development Committee of American Electric Power Company, developed a fund-raising plan to secure pledges that would yield a stream of contributions over the next five years. These funds, combined with an annual allocation to be provided through the NAS for NAE assistance in management of the NRC, would provide a reasonably secure base for the Academy's operation and growth.

Eric A. Walker
NAE president, 1966–1970

Establishing an Identity

As soon as he could, Walker turned his attention to raising public consciousness of the accomplishments of engineering and the work of engineers. The Academy's Council had established a Project Committee charged with reviewing all project requests and recommending Council action. Walker built on this concept, and with the assistance of NAE's Assistant Secretary Kerstin B. Pollack, who had also come from the Engineering Foundation and continued to work on Academy programs for some twenty years, the program mechanism was set in motion.

A Committee on Public Engineering Policy (COPEP) was formed in 1966 as a counterpart of a similar NAS committee that had already gained considerable visibility for NAS. Walker saw in this committee the potential for advising the government on public policy questions with an engineering component. One of COPEP's first formal studies was in response to a request from the House Committee on Science and Astronautics as it prepared legislation to create the congressional Office of Technology Assessment. After conducting a series of experimental technology assessments, COPEP reported that useful assessment methods were available and could help policymakers to secure the greatest value from technology.

Walker's early initiatives quickly gathered momentum as the NAE was recognized by some parts of the government as a ready source of advice on technological questions. NAE soon was setting up multiple *ad hoc* committees and conducting studies in response to government requests in addition to its work within the NRC.

Walker's own experience in underwater acoustics and naval ord-

The space shuttle was designed as a new way of launching payloads into space—with a reusable transporter. An external fuel tank, shown here, provides propellant for the shuttle's three main engines before it is jettisoned and burns up as it reenters the earth's atmosphere.

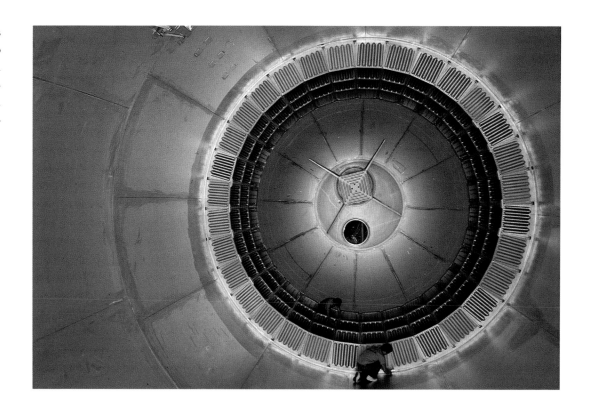

H. Guyford Stever

nance led him to encourage studies by, and increase the efforts of, the NAE Committee on Ocean Engineering established in 1965. Following a charge to "provide advice concerning our national capability to accomplish marine and maritime objectives," the committee (later the Marine Board) addressed coastal waste management and contributed to the International Decade of Ocean Exploration. Over the years, the board became a forum for the ocean engineering community to assess the development and use of ocean resources.

At another frontier, the Aeronautics and Space Engineering Board was established in 1967 at the request of the National Aeronautics and Space Administration (NASA). In 1968 an early assessment of the federal government's involvement in civil aviation R&D was conducted through this board under the chairmanship of NAE member and then president of Carnegie Mellon University H. Guyford Stever. Six committees were organized; each examined the role of government in supporting and advancing civil aviation in a specific area. Seven reports were issued, including a summary of the work of the six committees, recommending specific improvements in such problem areas as air traffic control, airport support facilities, and noise abatement.

The following year, the board began a significant advisory review program that provided NASA with an outside view of the fledgling space shuttle program. Under the chairmanship of NAE member Raymond L. Bisplinghoff, dean of M.I.T.'s school of engineering, the board addressed such key issues as the shuttle's size and payload requirements, sequential or concurrent booster/orbiter development, and the important technological questions involved in materials, structures, and thermal protection. The ensuing dialogue between NAE and NASA provided guidelines that contributed to the development of the program.

These activities took place during a period of leadership transition inside the NAS and amidst overriding public concern about the Vietnam war. Seitz, who held positions on the Defense Science Board, the President's Science Advisory Committee, and other organizations, came under attack from certain scientists in and out of the NAS. In an exasperated response to members of an NAS group opposing a military contract, Seitz pointed out that "the Academy was created to serve the government. I don't know where the government ends and the Department of Defense begins."

Philip Handler

The agitation generated by the Vietnam war continued throughout the Seitz administration. The *National Journal*, a news and opinion periodical published in Washington, D.C., reported that "From 1965 on there was a growing vocal group in the NAS which didn't want to have anything to do with the Defense Department. They split that organization right down the middle . . . ."

Seitz left in 1969 before his term was up to accept an invitation to succeed Bronk as head of The Rockefeller University. He was succeeded as president of the NAS by Philip Handler, a distinguished biochemist from Duke University and an active member of the NAS Council.

As its new president, Handler sought to broaden and strengthen the range of NAS activity. To do this, he initiated a restructuring of the NRC, adding to its traditional disciplinary divisions other, more flexible, entities organized along more problem-oriented lines. He also created mechanisms to ensure the election of more social and behavioral scientists into the NAS, and in 1970 helped fashion the Institute of Medicine in response to growing pressure from the clinical medicine community for an independent entity to address the health care problems of the nation. Finally, he had to work out a

Clarence H. Linder
NAE president, 1970–1973

Chauncey Starr

satisfactory relationship with the National Academy of Engineering, which had grown continuously more restive during the latter half of Seitz's administration.

A House Divided

As president of NAE since 1966, Walker was the key figure in this restlessness. He met with Handler on several occasions to seek a basis for cooperation and concluded that Handler had strong reservations about the direction the NAE was taking. As Walker recalls, Handler told him he thought that NAE was growing too fast—its membership had reached a level of approximately 100 in 1969—and that some members were being elected because they were heads of major corporations rather than because of their personal accomplishments in engineering.

Walker firmly believed that only a separate organization could guarantee an appropriate status for the engineering profession, but his attempts to get the NAE membership to support a move to separate from the NAS ended in failure. According to Walker, not more than twenty percent of the NAE members were willing to leave the NAS. Seeing no opportunity to advance his cause, Walker decided not to run for a second term and left the presidency of NAE when his four-year term was completed.

In 1970 NAE elected Clarence H. Linder its first full-time president (NAS had made its presidency a full-time position in 1965); Chauncey Starr was elected vice president. Linder, a founding member of the NAE, had spent his entire professional career with General Electric Company and had retired as vice president and group executive of the electric utilities group. Soft-spoken and dedicated to the welfare of engineering, he found himself also at odds with Handler.

Handler expressed the NAS's concern about the NAE in a number of letters to Linder. In one letter he noted the problem of potential conflict of interest arising from the industrial base of its membership and the problem of having pure science overshadowed by excessive reliance on the use of "handbook" science. On top of that, NAS leadership favored the merging of NAE programs into the NRC, a concept that did not appeal to many NAE members. The engineers felt that issues primarily involving engineering should be left solely to engineers and the NAE. They also wanted a clear agreement on the principles and details that would govern the work of the NRC.

Cooperative Studies

Even as internal differences were worsening, the two Academies were cooperating on a number of important—even explosive—issues, many dealing with sensitive topics such as the environment. The Environmental Studies Board, established in 1967 as a joint activity of the two Academies, continued to produce major reports on high-visibility topics. These included a 1971 study for the Port of New York Authority on ways to minimize the environmental impact of the then-proposed expansion of Kennedy Airport into Jamaica Bay; a 1973 study of the biological consequences of increases in solar ultraviolet radiation; and a 1974 multivolume report for the U.S. Senate Committee on Public Works assessing the adverse health effects of air pollutants, the relation of automotive emissions to ambient air quality, and the costs and benefits associated with control of automotive emissions.

In 1970 under President Linder, the NAE had established a committee chaired by W. Deming Lewis, president of Lehigh University, and including NAS member and environmentalist René Dubos, to take a long-term look at the problem of power plant (including nuclear) sitings. The committee took as its charge the development and definition of a rational framework for an approach to an emotion-charged issue that was creating hostility between

The interaction of sunlight with hydrocarbons and oxides of nitrogen in automotive exhaust stimulates the production of ozone, a principal cause of urban air pollution.

utility companies and environmentalists. Other contemporary "hot potatoes" in the NAE and NRC, as the *National Journal* put it, ranged from drug efficacy and government patent policy to the effects of low-level radiation and the use of defoliants in Vietnam.

This period also saw the publication of a series of significant NAE reports. In 1973 the NAE Committee on Telecommunications issued a highly significant report—*Telecommunications Research in the United States and Selected Foreign Countries*—that foreshadowed major concerns about industrial innovation in the 1980s. Among the study's conclusions was the observation that the United States was doing well in research but needed to concentrate on the application of research in products and services to remain competitive in world markets. In the same year, the results of a series of earlier reports by the NAE Committee on the Interplay of Engineering with Biology and Medicine (CIEBM) on sensory aids for the visually and hearing impaired were cited in testimony made to both houses of Congress. In addition, at congressional oversight hearings on what was to become the Vocational Rehabilitation Service, results of a CIEBM study of the use of aerospace technology in the civilian biomedical field were entered into the record, thereby contributing to the shaping of legislation that affected the subsequent course of rehabilitation services.

Bruce S. Old

Even as Linder was working to promote these and other Academy program efforts, he was concerned about the financial health of his institution. In May 1973 the NAE established the National Academy of Engineering Foundation (later Fund) to receive and disburse funds, beyond those being provided by the NAS, in support of the Academy's activities. Also during Linder's term, the office of the foreign secretary and a Committee on International Activities were created in 1970 in recognition of the importance of international engineering activities. Under the leadership of its first foreign secretary, Bruce S. Old, the NAE committee worked closely with the NAS and its foreign secretary in assessing and responding to international science and technology concerns.

The Struggle for Autonomy Continues

Under Walker, and later Linder, as NAE's program activities increased—NAE's annual program support from government contracts had reached approximately $1 million—the struggle between NAE and NAS over autonomy and organizational governance continued. In May 1971, apparent concern over the rapid growth in NAE programs and a general failure of the two institutions to arrive at a mutually agreeable operating mode led to the establishment of a negotiating team made up of both NAS and NAE members charged with reporting to the leadership on resolving the differences between the Academies over the operation of the NRC.

On January 10, 1973, the negotiating team presented several points that were described as "maximum possible convergence of institutional positions." The team proposed an agreement whereby each Academy would delegate substantial authority to the Governing Board of the NRC, whose actions would be final after a majority vote, even in matters with substantial engineering content. They also agreed that "no advisory program activities would be carried out outside of NRC except as specifically provided for." Under this arrangement, NAE would continue to exist within the NAS corporate structure, and NAS would ensure its financial stability, continuity, and identity as a separate membership body. A draft cover letter to the report closed with a clear notice that "should the two councils reject the report . . . then the succeeding question should not be whether separation should occur but rather how it should be accomplished."

The statement proved to be prophetic. The NAS asked for modifications in the agreement. The NAE Council thought it had compromised enough and refused to make them. Finally, on March 26, 1973, after much dialogue between the two bodies, the NAE Council decided to recommend to its members that they dissolve the nine-year partnership with the National Academy of Sciences and authorize the National Academy of Engineering to reorganize itself as an independent, nonprofit organization. The proposal was to be voted on by the full membership at the next annual meeting. Linder, who had been in the middle of this apparently irresolvable conflict since his term as Walker's vice president, had sought for some time to resign the presidency. It was his belief that the best interests of the NAE would be served by a new president, one not directly involved in the current controversy and who could bring a fresh perspective to the issues. In May 1973 Linder left his position as NAE president.

Reorganization and Rapprochement

Clearly, if the NAE structure was to remain intact, another person of experience and sensitivity was needed to take over the presidency. Fortunately, Robert C. Seamans, Jr., Secretary of the Air Force and a member of the NAE, was at that moment seeking to sever his relationship with the Nixon administration and was casting about for a new challenge. The NAE Council approached Seamans about the presidency, and he accepted.

The Council regarded Seamans, an aeronautical engineer from M.I.T., as unusually well equipped to step into the middle of this crisis. As associate and later deputy administrator of NASA, positions he held from 1960 to 1968, Seamans had faced and resolved numerous internal differences. Throughout the critical years of the man-in-space program, Seamans had come to be known as a problem solver who could keep NASA's program going steadily forward. He had organized several space studies that supported President John F. Kennedy's decision to place a man on the moon before the end of the decade. Seamans subsequently testified before Congress on many occasions to justify the $20-billion funding for the Apollo space project.

As Secretary of the Air Force in the Nixon administration, Seamans had helped reform procurement practices for major weapons systems. However, the emerging Watergate trauma in the early 1970s, added to the tensions of the Vietnam war and other frustrations with the Nixon administration, brought him to the edge of resignation and led to his quick acceptance of the new post as fourth president of NAE. On May 16, 1973, he issued a press release from the offices of the NAE announcing his election to the NAE presidency.

Tension was high at the first membership meeting over which Seamans presided in October 1973. The focus was on the brewing dissension between the two Academies. Seamans introduced the *pro forma* motion that Linder had prepared for the engineering academy to secede. But even as he gave it he realized that most NAE members really did not want to make such a radical move. Indeed they expressed their reluctance when they supported a motion by Eberhardt Rechtin, president of the Aerospace Corporation, to give Seamans six months to try to iron out the problems between the Academies.

This moratorium proved to be all that Seamans needed. Having

Robert C. Seamans, Jr.
NAE president, 1973–1974

received a significant number of supporting letters from members, Seamans drafted a letter to Handler proposing that the NAE continue to operate under the NAS charter. He approached Handler informally and asked if Handler would receive the letter, observing, "If it's the right thing to do, it's never too late."

With Handler's cooperation, Seamans organized a plan to restructure the joint operation of the NRC by the two Academies. A "Statement of Principles," approved by the Executive Committee of the NAE Council on October 24, 1973, declared that all advisory activities of the Academies would be undertaken within the NRC, which would be reorganized into eight principal operating units, four "assemblies" and four "commissions." The assemblies, intended to be the foci for disciplinary activities, embraced the behavioral and social sciences, life sciences, and mathematical and physical sciences. An Assembly of Engineering was added to the NRC as a major unit to administer all of the NAE programs. The president of the NAE was to be chairman of this assembly as well as vice chairman of the NRC. The commissions were to be multidisciplinary bodies concerned with problems having signficant societal implications. They included human resources, international relations, natural resources, and sociotechnical systems. The chairman of each commission would be appointed by the chairman of the NRC (president of NAS).

This complex organization, using the volunteer services of thousands of scientists and engineers, would be governed by a thirteen-person Governing Board consisting of seven representatives from the NAS (including the president and vice president), four members of the NAE (including the president and vice president), and two members of the Institute of Medicine (including the president). The Statement of Principles emphasized that "the restructured NRC is expected to become truly a single 'working arm' of both Academies. Accordingly . . . the Academies . . . will not establish or operate alternative, independent mechanisms for the conduct of studies which could be conducted appropriately within some element of the NRC." The principles recognized, however, that either Academy could initiate a program if all members of the committee appointed to deal with the issue were members of the sponsoring Academy.

The reorganization plan was not immediately satisfactory to either side. Among other issues, NAE was concerned over loss of visibility. During its brief nine years of existence, NAE had grown in stature as government agencies had learned to call on it for help in resolving engineering and technology issues. By July 1973 NAE's annual budget for administration and programs had grown to approximately $2 million. With twelve working boards and standing committees, the NAE had been making its presence known by tackling such high-visibility issues as the food/people balance, technology and international trade, priorities in applied research, and the application of technology to improve productivity in the service industries.

It was therefore understandable that some NAE leaders questioned at what price and for whose benefit these compromises were being made. After a rather long, heated debate, the reorganization was accepted. Although the NAS and NAE ended up essentially independent in the governance of their own affairs, the issue of balance of representation on the NRC Governing Board would remain unresolved. Moreover, it seemed to some observers that the NAS would dominate day-to-day operations and, because NAS controlled the bulk of the finances, it might continue to control the choice and direction of studies.

Despite the conflict and internal dissension, the NAE membership as a whole continued to support the concept of a joint NAS–NAE complex. In May 1974 when the NAE members voted on the restructured NAS governance, 385 ballots were cast. With 354 members voting to support "operation of the NAE as part of the NAS corporation," and only fourteen members voting for "separate" incorporation of the NAE, the membership had made an overwhelming statement of support for the new plan.

Program Activity

During this period of institutional furor, NAE continued to respond to government requests to study national issues. Seamans's aeronautical and space background was of use to the NAE's Space Applications Board (SAB) as it confronted issues of practical applications of space technology. In 1974 SAB conducted a user-oriented study that reviewed the state of satellite systems applications to fields including meteorology, agriculture, land-use planning, and environmental quality.

In some cases the two Academies continued to work closely together. A case in point was the early NAE response to the pending "energy crisis."

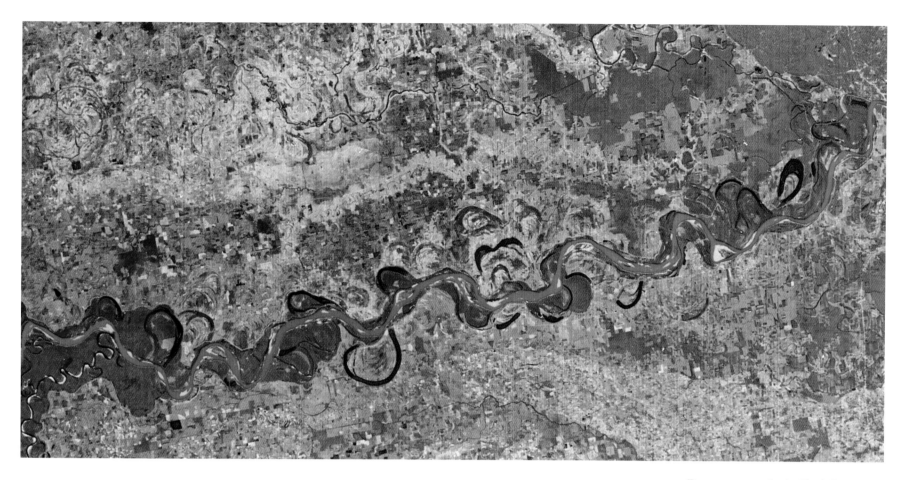

Remote sensors in the Earth Resources Technology Satellite-1 characterize land use along the Mississippi River from an altitude of 568 miles over southeast Arkansas, northeast Mississippi, and northeast Louisiana. Healthy crops and trees are shown in red; suburban areas, pink; barren land, gray; cities, green or dark gray; clear water, black or dark blue.

W. Kenneth Davis, vice president of the Bechtel Power Corporation, in early October 1973 told Seamans of his concern that the Academies were not doing enough to anticipate the difficulties bound to arise if the oil-producing countries in the Middle East cut off the U.S. energy supply. Seamans promptly made Davis the chairman of an NAE Task Force on Energy Program Planning to study the situation. On October 17 the OPEC oil embargo was imposed.

Davis pulled together a task force of NAE members, experts on energy, to design a study that could help set U.S. policy in the energy field. Seamans obtained Handler's support for the study, and the NAS provided funding. Since the NAE had conducted the study entirely through its own membership, the report, *U.S. Energy Prospects: An Engineering Viewpoint,* was released in May 1974 under its sole auspices.

According to Courtland D. Perkins, then chairman of the Department of Aeronautical Engineering at Princeton University and later president

What is to be the role of nuclear power in meeting the nation's future needs for energy?

of NAE, the study proved to be a timely contribution to the national dialogue on energy. It covered such topics as conservation, fossil fuels, nuclear energy, hydroelectric power, and novel sources such as solar and synthetic fuels. The experts showed clearly that President Richard M. Nixon's much-publicized objective of establishing U.S. energy independence by 1985, although within the realm of technical possibility, would at best be extremely costly and involve extensive redeployment of labor and capital with major adverse impacts on the economy as a whole.

On the education front, the NAE tackled one of the toughest problems faced by the engineering schools—how to encourage Blacks and other minority groups to choose engineering as a profession. In September 1973 NAE established a program to provide national leadership for an effort aimed at increasing the number of minority engineering graduates. A standing Committee on Minorities in Engineering and a National Advisory Council on Minorities in Engineering were organized to raise funds to provide scholarships for Blacks, Hispanics, and Native Americans and to act as a clearinghouse for jobs in industry and universities. In 1974 these activities were transferred to the NRC, and in 1980 the advisory committee was spun off into an independent organization, the National Action Council for Minorities in Engineering, which has become one of the most important entities in the United States fostering the entry of minority students into engineering careers. The NAE's deep involvement and catalytic role foreshadowed the impact NAE was to have on important engineering education concerns.

In July 1974, when the last pieces of the NAS–NAE restructuring agreement were finally in place, the importance of technology and engineering to the work of the NRC became clear. As NAE programs were shifted to the new NRC Assembly of Engineering, and the old NRC Division of Engineering took on a broader scope to become the Commission on Sociotechnical Systems, some twenty percent of the NRC's government-supported programs were readily recognizable as being technology based.

In late 1974 Seamans was offered a position as administrator of the new Energy Research and Development Administration. The legislation establishing this agency had been passed after Nixon's resignation and replacement by President Gerald R. Ford. Seamans accepted the post on December 29, 1974, and resigned the presidency of the NAE. William E. Shoupp, NAE vice president, took over the reins briefly while the Council searched for a new president. For the second time in less than two years, NAE had the difficult task of finding a new president and doing it rather rapidly if the gains of the early years were to be retained.

William E. Shoupp
Acting NAE president, 1974–1975

Strengthening the NAS–NAE Partnership

CHAPTER IV

Strengthening the NAS–NAE Partnership

James H. Mulligan, Jr.

The search committee formed to identify the NAE's fifth president seemed at first to have its work cut out for it on both the personal and policy levels. Not only would it be difficult to replace a man of Seamans's extraordinary qualifications and do it rapidly, but, as James H. Mulligan, Jr., then executive secretary of NAE, noted, the position required someone who could deal comfortably with the multiple constituencies of industry, government, and academia represented by the Academy membership. The job demanded managerial ability and a record of achievement that would be compatible with the high standards set for their members by the Academies. Most important, the engineers felt that the new president should be of sufficient stature to work on equal terms with the president of the NAS.

As NAE member Ralph Landau, then chairman of the high-tech engineering firm Halcon International and a member of the Council, recalls that period, the Council succeeded in finding an individual who had strong credentials in all three areas—industry, government, and academia. His name: Courtland D. Perkins.

Thomas C. Kavanagh, vice president of Louis Berger International, Inc., and past treasurer of NAE, chaired the search committee and put the offer to Perkins in April 1975. After considerable negotiation, it was agreed that Perkins would become the NAE president. Perkins accepted the nomination and was quickly elected by the Academy membership. He became at once president of NAE, vice chairman of NRC, and chairman of the NRC's Assembly of Engineering.

An aeronautical engineering graduate of Swarthmore and M.I.T. and a disciple of Theodore von Karman, Perkins had made important contributions in aerodynamics as a project engineer at Wright Field. He had moved on to become chairman of the Department of Aerospace Sciences at Princeton University and was serving as chairman of the Aerospace Department and associate dean of the Engineering School at the time of his election to NAE's presidency. Before taking the Princeton posts, Perkins had had a noteworthy career in the Air Force, as chief scientist and as assistant secretary for R&D in the last year of the Eisenhower administration. He also served as a consultant to a number of aerospace corporations. A man of conservative instincts who carried himself with dignity and humor, he was regarded as one who could help build the NAE without rekindling the antagonism that had marked the earlier days.

Courtland D. Perkins
NAE president, 1975–1983

Building on Strengths

The last half of the decade of the 1970s was a time of healing between the two Academies. When Seitz left the presidency of the NAS in 1969 he had advised NAE not to think of factionalism and potential secession but rather to build on its strengths. Perkins agreed with that philosophy. He saw his mission as having three goals: to build NAE membership, to improve the Academy's financial resources, and to enhance the position and public visibility of the NAE.

The NAE membership in 1975 numbered 550, compared with 1,200 in the NAS. To build the intellectual strengths of the Academy, the NAE Council proposed an election quota of 100 new members a year for a few years and then a reduction in that rate until, by the year 2000, NAE membership would approximate that of the NAS.

But how to identify the proper engineers for election? The U.S. community of engineers included many individuals who would have been brought into membership during their active years if the NAE had been in existence at the time. Unfortunately, membership rules specified that only active engineers could be admitted, and many nominations had been rejected solely on that basis. Perkins appealed to the Council to change the criteria used by the membership committee to allow for the nomination and election of "old-timers" in the engineering field. The Council agreed to make the change, thus opening NAE membership to a generation of distinguished engineers. By the time he retired as president in 1983, Perkins's first goal had been met—the NAE had doubled its membership to 1,100 compared with the NAS's 1,350.

During Perkins's presidency another membership milestone was passed when the NAE followed NAS's example and elected the first distinguished engineers from abroad to be foreign associates of the Academy. By 1989, its twenty-fifth anniversary year, the Academy listed over 125 foreign associates, approximately eight percent of its membership, thereby broadening its reach internationally.

Perkins also took direct aim at the problem of independent financial resources of the Academy. The only resources NAE could call its own came from the receipt of membership dues set at $100 per year and a modest endowment made up primarily of gifts contributed by friends, mostly members of the Council, and the remainder of the original fund-raising efforts of Walker and Sporn. Perkins felt that the Academy of Engineering would never speak effectively within the Academy complex if it failed to carry its share of the institution's operating expenses and instead continued to draw more than seventy-five percent of its financial support through the NAS.

The situation was especially ironic because the NAE membership included executives from some of the most successful corporations in the country. With the approval of the Council, Perkins and Donald N. Frey, chairman of the board and president of Bell and Howell and chairman of the NAE Development Committee, initiated a campaign based on a simple fund-raising technique that had worked well for Perkins at Princeton: approach a potential donor and ask point-blank for money.

Perkins launched the campaign by appealing to five industry chief executive officers for grants of $50,000 to $100,000 spread over a five-year period. He delivered letters personally to each chief executive officer, explaining why he thought the contribution was important to the future of engineering. This sortie netted pledges amounting to $400,000. That success led Perkins to raise his funding objective to $3 million. Of the sixty major U.S. companies Perkins ultimately contacted, fifty-two came through with grants, and, by 1983, when Perkins completed his last term as president, with discretionary spending held to a modest level, the NAE endowment had grown to $5.2 million. Although still a far cry from the NAS endowment, it nevertheless represented a significant commitment to engineering and the beginning of financial independence for the NAE.

During his term Perkins took several actions to enhance the public visibility of engineering—his third goal. Availing himself of a section in the 1973 restructuring agreement that allowed for the initiation of independent NAE study committees, provided their entire membership came from the NAE, Perkins secured Council approval and used a small portion of NAE's independent resources to fund roundtables, or quick-turnaround studies. These studies addressed such technology-charged topics as competitiveness in the U.S. civil aviation industry and guidelines for the reauthorization of the Clean Water Act, an important piece of environmental legislation that was the subject of considerable social and political debate.

Engineering education was the focus of a 1980 report issued by the NAE under the chairmanship of NAE member Bruno A. Boley, then dean of

Rapid growth of air travel in foreign markets implies important opportunities in export sales for the U.S. aircraft industry.

The Technological Institute and Walter P. Murphy Professor of Engineering, Northwestern University. The task force on engineering education in its report, *Issues in Engineering Education: A Framework for Analysis,* recommended among other things the development of special postbaccalaureate student programs in engineering and an updating of teaching and research facilities.

In addition to these studies, Perkins continued the tradition of devoting one day of each Academy annual meeting to a symposium addressing critical issues in the engineering community. During the 1979 annual meeting, for example, the symposium assessed the outlook for nuclear power, and the 1981 symposium attempted one of the first interdisciplinary looks at genetic engineering and the role engineers would play in the problems of scaling up laboratory processes to fully operational commercial ventures.

The last symposium of the Perkins presidency, held in 1983, assessed the long-term impact of technology on employment and unemployment. The symposium served as the basis for a major study later conducted in the Committee on Science, Engineering, and Public Policy, a joint committee of the NAS, NAE, and IOM.

Concern for U.S. Industrial Competitiveness

In the mid-1970s, Perkins lent his support to one of the most far-reaching series of studies initiated by the NAE. The series began as a result of several discussions among N. Bruce Hannay, vice president of research at Bell Laboratories and NAE foreign secretary from 1976 to 1984; Hugh H. Miller, the executive director of the NAE office of the foreign secretary; and NAE member John V. N. Granger, who at the time was deputy assistant secretary for science and technology at the U.S. Department of State. The focus of their concern was the diminishing leadership of the United States in world technology. U.S. productivity growth was lower than that of other industrialized countries and appeared to be steadily declining. Industrial plants were aging. The nation's historically positive trade balance was turning negative, and, most telling, U.S. trade in technology-intensive products such as electronics and automobiles started to reflect a shrinking share of world markets.

Hannay and Miller decided that an analysis of this situation was warranted and assembled a task force of experts, including as chairman Milton Katz, Henry L. Stimson Professor of Law and director of international

N. Bruce Hannay

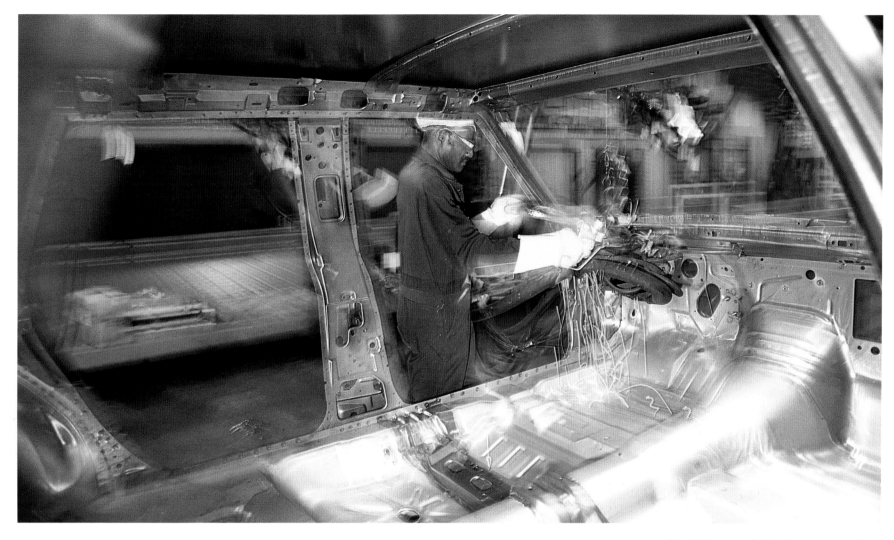

The U.S. automobile industry responds to foreign competition with technological innovation and progressive management practices.

legal studies at Harvard Law School and a former director of the Marshall Plan, and NAE members Ralph Landau and Lewis M. Branscomb, vice president and chief scientist, IBM Corporation. Opposition soon developed from those who thought NAE was overreaching itself by attempting to discuss technology issues in the industrial and economic context of public policy, but Hannay persisted. To enable the study to draw on the broadest range of experts, regardless of NAE membership, and in compliance with the 1973 agreement with the NAS, NAE housed the committee in the NRC, with NAE oversight.

Technology, Trade, and the U.S. Economy, published in 1978, concluded that U.S. performance in world trade was determined much less by events outside the United States than by the health of the domestic economy and the

The textile industry, still labor-intensive, faces a shortage of technical workers and managers to remain competitive in the international marketplace.

constraints on it. To consider this conclusion in greater depth, the task force, which was reconstituted as the Committee on Technology and International Economic and Trade Issues, conducted a series of workshops to examine the effects of various government policies on technological innovation and U.S. competitiveness. In 1976 Granger became deputy associate director of NSF for science, technology, and international affairs, and was instrumental in securing a long-term commitment of funds from NSF. The NSF support helped plow new ground not only in NAE but also in NSF, where such funding was one of that agency's early excursions into engineering and technology policy topics.

The focus of the workshops was well defined—federal tax policies, government regulation, and antitrust policies and their effect on technological innovation. The findings and recommended policy changes to increase industrial innovation and productivity were set forth in a set of monographs based on the workshops.

According to Hannay, these studies were among the earliest to examine these issues in depth. By opening dialogues in policymaking quarters, they fed into the national debate on tax policy and its effect on innovation, debate that ultimately resulted in the enactment of a reduction in the capital gains tax in 1978, a move initially opposed by the Carter administration. Perhaps most important, venture capital available to new enterprises immediately showed a significant increase, a change attributed by many economists primarily to the decrease in the capital gains tax.

Hannay arranged a series of meetings with Frank Press, science and technology adviser to the president and director of the Office of Science and Technology Policy in the Carter administration. Press was sensitive to the concerns expressed in the studies. One result was that the White House asked the Department of Commerce to review the effect of government policy on industrial innovation. This was done by a task force headed by NAE member Jordan J. Baruch, assistant secretary of commerce for science and technology. The report, *The President's Industrial Innovation Initiatives*, was issued in 1979.

In December 1979 the growing national interest in problems related to industrial innovation led the NAE to hold a major colloquium titled "Industrial Innovation and Public Policy Options." Chaired by NAE member Arthur M. Bueche, senior vice president for corporate technology, General

Electric Company, the two-day colloquium attracted representatives from industry, academe, and government, together with experts involved in major innovation studies, research, and policymaking, to discuss the major policy issues affecting innovation.

The success of the earlier workshops and policy studies on competitiveness and government policy ensured continuing NSF funding and led to the creation in 1979 of six panels to investigate the competitive position of selected U.S. industries—textiles, steel, machine tools, pharmaceuticals, automobiles, and electronics. A seventh study, an assessment of the U.S. civil aviation manufacturing industry, followed in 1983, with funding from NASA through the NSF. Requiring six years to complete, these studies involved the volunteer efforts of more than 100 experts in such diverse fields as labor, environmental and industrial technology, manufacturing, and business, and were managed by study director Marlene (Phillips) Beaudin.

Each industry had a different set of problems and depended on new technology and government policies in different ways to advance its competitive position. In the first study, of the automobile industry, the panel found that, contrary to popular belief, technology was not the major key to the Japanese advantage—automobile technology had not changed significantly until the mid-1970s—rather, the advantage was due to management factors in Japanese plants and to cultural attitudes that led to superior and more cost-effective teamwork in inventory control, in quality control, and on the assembly line.

In the study of the pharmaceutical industry, a panel found a pronounced deterioration in the relative performance of the U.S. pharmaceutical industry in relation to its Europe counterparts despite the industry's basic profitability, high growth rate, and technical accomplishments. The problems stemmed from the excessive time and expenditure required to bring a new drug to market in the United States. The panel recommended several changes in the regulatory process that could make the United States more competitive without compromising the goals of regulation.

In a summary of the seven industry reports, Hannay and committee member Lowell Steele, manager of R&D planning, General Electric Company, enumerated several common themes. The most significant finding was that all of the sectors examined had become world-scale industries,

Inexpensive new electronic devices such as microprocessors and sensors are opening up new opportunities for automation of production equipment in the machine tool industry.

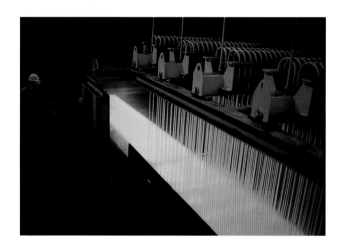

Technological leadership does not ensure economic success in the steel industry, where U.S. producers face a number of problems, including the inability to generate capital.

Walter A. Rosenblith

needing to be managed as such and requiring adjustments in public policy to reflect the pervasiveness of international competition. The series also brought to light a general lack of coherence and mutual reinforcement in U.S. policies and institutions. This was manifested in a lack of agreement on priorities and handicaps faced by small firms in pursuing international sales.

On the international front, in 1979, NAE Foreign Secretary Hannay joined the NAS Foreign Secretary Walter A. Rosenblith, also an NAE member, in establishing an NAS–NAE opening to China. These efforts resulted in a 1980 visit of an NAE delegation to China.

Governance of NRC

Yet even as the NAE strengthened its program efforts, internal dissatisfaction continued to plague NAS–NAE relations. And so, under Perkins another strong effort was made to increase even further the participation of the NAE in the operations and governance of the NRC.

Recognizing that engineering in the NRC was not limited to activities of the Assembly of Engineering and that NAE interests included work in science, manpower, international affairs, behavioral and social sciences, and education, Handler and Perkins agreed in February 1979 that the NAE president should no longer serve as chairman of an NRC operating unit. H. Guyford Stever, a member of both the NAS and the NAE, was then appointed chairman of the Assembly of Engineering.

In May 1980 Handler and Perkins, conscious of continuing undercurrents of dissatisfaction over the role of the NAE, convened a committee, similar to the one originally envisioned in the NAE Articles of Organization, to review the relationship of NAS and NAE. It was the first time such a group had been convened. The committee concluded with an endorsement of prior steps and, further, supported an increase in NAE participation in all National Research Council committees, not just the Assembly of Engineering. It was even suggested that the NAE president be brought more actively into the day-to-day operations of the NRC. To strengthen NAE finances, the committee recommended that, in parallel with NAS practice, a larger portion of NAE's administrative expense be supported by the NRC indirect costs in return for NAE's increasing oversight responsibilities.

These changes were important steps toward improving relations between NAS and NAE. Symbolic of this new cooperation and unity was the establishment of the National Academy Press at the behest of Robert M. White, then administrator of the NRC. The new logo for the Press, later adopted by the institution as a whole, displayed the abbreviations of the three member organizations in the Academy complex (NAS, NAE, IOM) bound together by the NRC.

Symbol of the National Academy Press

In summing up these accomplishments in an address at the NAE annual meeting in October 1980, Handler pointed out that engineers and scientists "are not exactly the same kind of animal. They. . . think somewhat differently, . . . see the world somewhat differently, [and] ask somewhat different questions." Nevertheless, they had come together in the National Research Council with a common purpose and a common goal—to serve the nation by working together. Handler reemphasized that to attain this common objective, both Academies had an interest in strengthening the NRC so that, as he put it, "the National Research Council will evolve further along this trail as a mechanism whereby American society can assemble the best of scientific and technical talent in the national interest."

Handler was succeeded in 1981 by Frank Press, former White House science and technology adviser, who was to become a key figure in the close partnership that came to characterize the Academies in the second half of the 1980s. A quiet-spoken though tough administrator with political acumen derived from high-level government experience, Press spent his first year reorganizing the NRC staff, streamlining committees, simplifying bureaucratic procedures, and reordering priorities. Even those staff members who revered Handler and enjoyed his free-wheeling style agreed that Press was a man who knew how to make things work.

Frank Press

In his role as chairman of the NRC, Press turned his attention early to the network of committees and boards of the NRC and to the NRC's day-to-day operations. Complaints of duplication and overlapping of functions had been surfacing for some time. Committee members and others had noted the omission of studies in important areas; other studies were not proceeding rapidly enough to satisfy interested government agencies.

Despite the Seamans-Handler agreement of 1973, real equality between NAS and NAE in deciding the affairs of the NRC continued to be elusive. The fact that the NRC Governing Board still numbered seven NAS members to four NAE members and two from IOM suggested that NAE remained far from fulfilling its potential as an equal in the governance of the NRC.

Sensitive to these concerns, in the fall of 1981, Press and Perkins established a cooperative *ad hoc* Committee on the Review of the NRC, charged with developing "a new organizational plan to better fit the real world in which the NRC operates in the 1980s." The committee was chaired by James D. Ebert, then director of the Carnegie Institution of Washington and vice president of the NAS, with members from both NAS and NAE.

What the Ebert Committee, as it came to be called, saw was that the compartmentalized structure of the NRC invited bureaucratic inefficiencies, and the committee set out to remedy them. Among the major changes was the consolidation and combination of engineering elements contained in several NRC units into a single Commission on Engineering and Technical Systems. This merger responded to the increasing concern with the societal nature of engineering problems and permitted the formation of committees and boards broad enough to address them.

Press had come quickly to the view that the NAE had a critical role to play in the Academy complex. He accepted and built on Handler's conclusion that the kinds of problems that came before the NRC could no longer be resolved along traditional lines—engineering versus science or industry versus academe. Instead, the complex, global challenges of the 1980s increasingly required the collaborative efforts of government, industry, and academe.

On September 16, 1982, just before his term of office ended, Perkins joined Press in an important step forward for the NAE. They signed a Memorandum of Understanding that further cemented the working relationships between the two Academies. The memorandum reaffirmed that the management of each Academy would be under the exclusive control of its council with regard to policies of staff or programs, as long as they did not affect the operations of the NRC.

The key provision of the memorandum, however, was for many the culmination of a nearly twenty-year effort. It revised the structure by which the NRC, the center of action of the Academies, would be governed. For the first time, there would be virtual equality between the two Academies in the governance of the NRC. Thirteen members would still be chosen for the NRC Governing Board, but there would be five from the NAS, five from the NAE, and two from IOM. The thirteenth member would be the president of the NAS serving as board chairman; and the president of the NAE, as one of the five, would continue to serve as NRC vice chairman. This agreement represented NAE's most important step in its long search for a more prominent role in the management of NRC.

NAE Studies, Membership, and Structure

As part of the final agreement, the NAE agreed to join with the NAS in using a portion of its independent funds to support joint, self-initiated studies that could address science and policy issues for which government support was not forthcoming. NAE also agreed to suspend its fund-raising effort for one year and to join the NAS in a program designed both to augment the institution's financial strength and to forge stronger links with industry. Thus the Academy Industry Program, which was patterned loosely after such cooperative programs as M.I.T.'s Industrial Liaison Program, was started.

By 1981 as the membership roll of the NAE had begun to approach that of the NAS, the NAE focused more closely on fundamental issues of membership policy. Recognizing that membership standards were of primary importance, the Academy turned to the application and interpretation of the criteria for membership and the original concerns such as maintenance of balance among academia, industry, and other sectors. In addition, the growth in membership brought new concerns about balance among the fields of engineering, the geographic and demographic distribution of members, and representation from large and small organizations.

On the recommendation of Home Secretary Harold Liebowitz, dean of engineering at George Washington University, Perkins, with the approval of the Council, established the *ad hoc* Committee on NAE Membership Elections; Liebowitz was appointed chairman and was assisted initially by E. Henriette Nelson and then by Virginia A. Harrison, executive assistants for membership. The committee recommended in April 1982 a comprehensive set of measures for achieving better balance in the election process and dealing with newly emerging or underrepresented engineering disciplines. It suggested guidelines to assist in determining the desirable size and distribution of the NAE membership and called for the establishment of a standing advisory committee on membership policy.

Harold Liebowitz

Ralph Landau

Stephen D. Bechtel, Jr.

The NAE Council approved the major recommendations of the *ad hoc* committee, including the establishment of the Membership Policy Committee. These actions put the NAE membership election process in a position to deal with the requirements of the larger, more diverse organization the NAE had become and to match the growing complexities and expanding domain of the engineering enterprise it was to serve.

Paralleling the structural changes that Press was making in the NRC, important structural changes were also being made in the NAE in recognition of its new responsibilities. Perhaps the most significant of these changes was the establishment of the position of NAE chairman—a part-time, elected post, to be filled by a member who was a leading industrialist. NAE Vice President Ralph Landau, who proposed the idea, recalls hearing early objections that such a move might weaken the presidency of the NAE and unduly institutionalize the role of industry. To those critics, Landau's response was that the concept was modeled after the administrative structure of many universities, which were often organized around a president and a chairman of the board of trustees.

The move had several objectives. One was to provide the growing Academy with a greater depth of leadership. A second was to strengthen the Academy's liaison with industry, a goal more easily achieved by a business leader. The chairman would occupy the chair of the NAE Council, while the president of NAE would serve as the chief executive officer. The chairman could also help in fund-raising, and, by staggering the chairman's terms of office with those of the president, could smooth the transitions between succeeding presidents of the NAE.

The first industrialist to be elected to the post was Stephen D. Bechtel, Jr., chairman of the Bechtel Group, an international engineering firm based in San Francisco. The Bechtel Group had built some of the world's largest and most complex facilities and structures and exemplified Bechtel's beliefs in the power of engineering. A dynamic leader with a modest, yet highly focused approach to technical and management problems, Bechtel brought to the NAE his strong belief in the importance of engineering expertise in meeting the needs of society.

Bechtel was elected chairman in 1982. His first task was to oversee the search for a president to succeed Perkins, who had agreed to extend his term as president by one year, in part to provide continuity and guidance during the major institutional reorganization. Aided by Edward R. Kane, then president of E. I. du Pont de Nemours & Company, the NAE search committee agreed to ask Robert M. White, then president of a university consortium operating the National Center for Atmospheric Research in Boulder, Colorado.

As former chief of the U.S. Weather Bureau in the Kennedy and Johnson administrations and first head of the National Oceanic and Atmospheric Administration, serving under presidents Nixon and Ford, White was familiar with the workings of government. He also knew the NAE. He had served on the NAE Council and had been chairman of the NRC Commission on Natural Resources as well as administrator of the NRC under Handler. A renowned meteorologist from Harvard and M.I.T., White was known for his global interests and research contributions that made him well qualified for the job of president at a time when NAE was taking its place on the world scene. White was elected by the membership and installed as president on July 1, 1983.

NAE Comes of Age

CHAPTER V

NAE Comes of Age

When Robert White, NAE's sixth president, took the helm in 1983, he found an organization with a rich history of programs, but still striving to make its presence felt on the national scene. The conflicts over NRC governance seemed far behind. The NAE had some 1,200 members, almost as many as the NAS. The NRC, the joint operating arm of the Academies and the IOM, comprised 1,000 employees and 9,000 study volunteers—the most influential private science and technology advisory organization in America.

Most important, NAS President Frank Press believed in a full and strong partnership between the two Academies. To Press, the differences between science and technology that had dominated the dialogue of the early years were now only a semantic hurdle. Not only was the specialized expertise of both groups important in responding to the complex challenges of the 1980s, but law, economics, and other disciplines outside the mainstream of the Academies were also necessary to any solution of world problems. As for NAE's immediate priorities, Press felt that any concern over image that may have lingered from the past should give way to a determination of how best to work together to restore and maintain American technological leadership in the world.

Although troubled by the continuing lack of visibility of the NAE, White agreed with Press. In many respects the two men were singularly matched—both having come from the related fields of earth and atmospheric sciences to leadership positions in the federal government. In practical terms, however, White came into office sensitive to the dissatisfaction among some engineers over the NAE's role in the conduct of programs and studies. Many members continued to feel that despite Press's supportive position, NAE was somehow lagging in matters of prestige and image among government agencies and in the media. As one NAE member put it, NAE was "invisible."

White took steps to alter the situation, some symbolic, others substantive. On the symbolic side, for instance, he struck a modest but visible blow for equality by accepting Press's offer and moving his office from a remote corner of the third floor to the second floor next door to Press. On the substantive side, he sought to ensure the continuation of positive relations with the NAS by encouraging cooperative activities among the institutional leaders. Executive meetings among the NAS, NAE, and IOM presidents became a regular occurrence.

During these early years of White's presidency, relations with the NAS flourished. One of the very few sharp divisions in policy views between the two Academies arose in 1984 over the role of engineering in the National Science Foundation. Since the inception of NSF, the engineering community had chafed at the level of support—only ten percent of the budget—afforded engineering research.

When NSF's enabling legislation came up for review by the Congress, the Academies entered the center of the controversy. Leading engineers urged amendment of the NSF's statutory language to place engineering on a par with science instead of regarding it as a branch of science. At the same time, engineers sought to change the name of the organization. White moved to lend the weight of NAE to this initiative.

As in Vannevar Bush's day, the science community was not ready to accept the concept; Frank Press opposed changes in the NSF's enabling legislation, arguing that NSF should give priority to the support of science even if it meant leaving the support of academic engineering largely in the hands of the mission-oriented agencies such as DOD and NASA. The political compromise in the Congress did not adopt the proposed change in the National Science Foundation name but did alter the statutory language to elevate engineering to the level of science.

Robert M. White
NAE president, 1983–

Gearing Up for NAE's Third Decade

The NAE also began to search for new outlets for its energies. At a summer retreat meeting in August 1983, Bechtel led the NAE Council in a detailed assessment of the major issues that would move the NAE more forcefully toward its broader goal, namely, that of making the Academy a strong force for advancing the role of engineering and technology in the United States.

Out of that effort came a formal statement designed to guide the work of the institution through its third decade. The Council codified the Decade III program into a set of goals encompassing all aspects of the Academy operation from programs and administration to membership elections and financial needs.

In the same year, White, convinced that it was now time for NAE to strengthen its contributions to the public debate on national policy issues and to enhance its national identity, proposed a series of NAE symposia and studies to survey the broad impact of technology on society and determine which problems required special attention. Funding of $750,000 was obtained from Carnegie Corporation of New York and The Andrew W. Mellon Foundation. The NAE's Technology and Social Priorities series, as it was called, proved to be a major step in revitalizing NAE's roster of program activities dealing with major public policy issues and in helping to focus national attention on those issues.

Over the next two years the issues discussed included an in-depth look at the question of liability and fairness involved in technological disasters similar to the 1984 chemical explosion in Bhopal, India (*Hazards: Technology and Fairness*); an assessment of advances made in high-tech medical devices (*New Medical Devices: Invention, Development, and Use*); and a survey of the social, economic, and technological forces that shape the nation's infrastructure needs (*Cities and Their Vital Systems*).

It was during this time that the elements of a longer-term program came into focus based on the NAE Council's belief that U.S. technological leadership and competitiveness continued to be an overriding national economic concern. As White portrayed it in a 1986 talk to members, "If the Soviet launch of *Sputnik* was a technological shock and the oil crisis of 1973 an oil shock, then what is happening to us today can only be called a competitiveness shock."

The question for NAE was clear. Could it propose and implement programs that could alter national policies to overcome the ten-year decline in international competitiveness of U.S. industries? To provide answers to the question, Bechtel suggested bringing together national industrial leaders into an Industry Advisory Board to help enumerate the most important long-range technology-oriented issues that would face the nation in the next decade and to consider the kinds of programs that would deal with them.

During 1985 the details of a program directed toward improving American competitiveness through enhancing the quality of U.S. engineering were crystallized. In March 1985 President Ronald Reagan sent a personal message encouraging the NAE to "marshal the nation's technical engineering-based expertise in a campaign that will ensure America's scientific, technological and engineering leadership into the 21st century." With this endorsement the Technological Leadership Program, later expanded into the full-fledged Technology Agenda to Meet the Competitive Challenge, moved ahead.

Alexander H. Flax

Under the combined leadership of NAE Home Secretary Alexander H. Flax, program office director Jesse H. Ausubel, and associate director Bruce R. Guile, who succeeded Ausubel as director in 1988, the Agenda considered technology in its broadest sense, encompassing interrelationships of engineering with economics, management, government, environment, and other fields as they affected industrial and financial operations. The Technology Agenda Program, as it came to be called, was defined through three primary themes—technology and economic growth in a global environment, engineering research and education, and public awareness.

The promotion of membership involvement in planning the work of the NAE now became one of White's major concerns. Committees had been a part of the NAE structure since its founding. Committees had conducted studies, raised and managed funds, and set membership policies. Now, with the Decade III goals defined, an oversight structure was essential to guide the work of the Academy. Bechtel's original suggestion of establishing an Industry Advisory Board was soon followed with an Education (later Academic) Advisory Board with membership from all levels of academic community leadership, a Technology and Society Committee to aid in program planning, an International Affairs Advisory Committee, and a Public Awareness Advisory Committee.

W. Dale Compton

Edward R. Kane

Frederic A. L. Holloway

With a program staff and committee-based advisory apparatus in place, the 1983 goals of the Council now appeared to be within reach. A Fellows program was instituted to bring talented young professionals to the NAE, and senior fellows provided high-level experience to energize and guide NAE programs. NAE member W. Dale Compton, former vice president for research at Ford Motor Company, came to the Academy in 1986 as its first Senior Fellow.

A program as ambitious as the NAE Technology Agenda required substantial resources. To provide them, Steve Bechtel and Ralph Landau in 1984 launched the NAE 25th Anniversary Fund Drive, which set a goal of raising $30 million over five years, culminating with the twenty-fifth anniversary of the Academy in December 1989. Starting with an asset base of $5.2 million, Bechtel and Landau, assisted by the NAE Development Office under the direction of Jeanne G. Jacob, mobilized the efforts of many members and other individuals, private corporations, and foundations to secure sufficient short-term funds to support a $2-million-a-year program effort as well as to provide longer-term operating reserves.

By the NAE's twenty-fifth anniversary, more than $40 million had been raised, made up of independent and program funds and "bricks and mortar" contributions. Under the stewardship of treasurers Frederic A. L. Holloway and later Edward Kane, the NAE would mark the end of its first quarter century with approximately $20 million in assets and an annual administrative and program budget of $5 million, of which about two-thirds came from NAE independent funds.

With the funding goals established, White concentrated on the internal structure of the NAE. By 1985 the staff had doubled. Operating functions were divided into offices, and new management tools were introduced. A more effective budgeting and asset-management structure was instituted under the leadership of Marlene Beaudin, director of administration and finance.

Throughout the years, the prestige of the NAE has derived from the quality of its members. Over the course of more than twenty years, however, the mechanism by which the membership selection was made—the election process—had grown complex and cumbersome. The conduct of the election itself was loosely organized and poorly controlled. Moreover, the membership at large had little knowledge of the procedures. To remedy these problems, White asked Ralph E. Fadum, dean of engineering at North Carolina State University and chairman of the Committee on Membership, and Home Secretary Flax to draft a codification of policies and procedures for elections. With the assistance of Deborah K. Brandt, director of the membership office, a definitive guide for the NAE election process was first published in 1985 and is updated periodically.

Another of the Council's concerns and Academy goals was to improve the public identity of the NAE. On the whole, members were content with the public recognition accorded them by membership, but some remained concerned about the perceived sacrifice of public visibility that had occurred in 1974 when the NAE transferred most of its independent engineering projects to the NRC Assembly of Engineering. The members believed that in the eyes of the media, and thus the eyes of the public, the NRC was the NAS and not the operating arm of both Academies.

Bechtel's interest in improving public awareness of engineering and technology had led him to urge the creation of a public awareness advisory group within the NAE, charged with promoting "the greater appreciation of the part that engineering and technology play in the nation's welfare." To Bechtel, public awareness had several elements, namely, promotion of the work of the NAE, increased public understanding of the importance of engineering and technology to the quality of life, and improved communications among the spokesmen of the engineering community—the engineering societies. Under the guidance of an NAE Public Awareness Advisory Committee, the NAE effort was begun. Over the next few years under the direction of NAE Public Awareness Officer Carrie Levandoski, activities grew to include an engineering outreach program, addressing issues of importance to the profession; responsibility for the administration of NAE awards; publication and dissemination of articles, papers, and background materials in various engineering disciplines; and regular liaison with government staff to provide lawmakers with useful information about technology and the work of the NAE.

In the past, even though NAE was in part created by the engineering societies and had held occasional meetings with some of them, it had kept its distance, seeing itself as an adviser to the government and not as an umbrella for coordination of activities of the engineering community. Now, with its federal advisory role assured, the NAE began to assess this view as limiting and moved to establish an annual convocation of professional engineering societies as a forum for review of common problems. A commitment of financial and other support was made, aimed at broadening the activities of National Engineers' Week, a national celebration of the engineering profession established by the National Society of Professional Engineers, and the Junior Engineering Technical Society program. These activities, administered by NAE Executive Officer William C. Salmon, strengthened NAE's links with the national engineering community.

Developing a Global Point of View

In 1986 Bechtel completed his second term as chairman. The NAE membership then turned for its second chairman to John (Jack) F. Welch, Jr., the hard-driving chief executive officer of General Electric Company. Welch brought his world view to NAE, noting that "alliances will be forged with every significant global industry—medical, autos, defense, materials, and so on. Those who are slow to recognize the emergence of these global alliances or to join in forming them will find themselves locked out of the game as we enter the 1990s."

John F. Welch, Jr.

This view came at a critical time. For nearly a decade, studies in the NAE and throughout the Academies had buttressed the idea that technology is the key to economic growth and a higher standard of living. In Welch this message had another strong proponent. NAE adopted as a general program theme the relationship of technology to economic growth and systematically explored this theme through a series of symposia and studies. In 1985 the role played by technology in competitiveness on a global scale was examined from differing viewpoints under Landau's leadership in a joint project with Stanford University. *The Positive Sum Strategy: Harnessing Technology for Economic Growth* brought NAE recognition in the economic as well as the engineering communities and has been used in courses in several leading universities.

In 1987, under the chairmanship of James Brian Quinn of Dartmouth's Amos Tuck School of Business, the NAE instituted a pioneering technological and economic examination of the $2.5-trillion services industry. Over the years this sector—which includes communications, health care, financial services, and transportation—had been a plus on the economy's

Automatic teller machines provide a process innovation that changes the way financial institutions deliver their product—the client-teller transaction.

trade balance ledger, but in the 1980s even these industries' trade balance turned slightly negative in part because of the growing technological sophistication of services in competitive countries. "Services are really high-tech industries," White pointed out. "They are the greatest consumers of high-tech products and require the backup of high-tech institutions."

NAE continued to address questions related to industrial competition. In 1988 questions such as "What lessons were to be learned from corporations that were successful in bringing products to market and from those that were unsuccessful?" stimulated the NAE to launch a study to probe the process. The project, entitled "Profiting from Innovation," was led by NAE Senior Fellow William G. Howard, Jr., senior vice president and director of research at Motorola.

Engineering Research and Education

Another way in which NAE contributed to the ideas that underlie policy formulation was its recognition of the insistent need to strengthen the nation's engineering research and education systems—the bedrock of the nation's technological future. For instance, both the NAE and the NSF were concerned in the early 1980s that U.S. engineering education in manufacturing had not kept pace with changes in world industry, which was emphasizing cost-effective integration of design, engineering, manufacturing, and marketing. The lack of a corresponding emphasis in U.S. engineering education contributed to the fact that many industries in other nations were able to bring innovations to commercial markets faster than U.S. industry.

This concern surfaced in 1983 when several members of the Academies' Committee on Science, Engineering, and Public Policy met in the office of George A. Keyworth III, then science and technology adviser to President Reagan. The meeting had been called to discuss computers in design and manufacturing, but, according to Keyworth, the engineers present—including NAE members Roland W. Schmitt and George M. Low—soon realized that they were dealing with not just one area of computer-based technology but a sweeping revolution in engineering wrought by the combination of computers and automation, as in computer-aided design and in process simulation.

Out of this realization came a call by Keyworth at the 1983 NAE Annual Meeting to take action in establishing new modes of partnership between universities, industry, and government through the medium of engineering research centers (ERCs) on selected university campuses. The idea was that such centers might lead the way to greater effectiveness of U.S. industrial companies and at the same time improve the education of the engineering student. An NAE study chaired by W. Dale Compton resulted in a 1984 report, *Guidelines for Engineering Research Centers: A Report to the National Science Foundation.*

By 1989 there were eighteen NSF-sponsored ERCs on campuses around the country. These centers have been designed as interdisciplinary engineering research partnerships between universities and industry to promote the speedier transformation of research ideas into useful technology and in turn to produce the talent essential to meet world competition.

Roland W. Schmitt   George M. Low

Typical of the centers now in operation is the Engineering Center for Telecommunications Research at Columbia University. There some fifty graduate students explore advanced communications systems that carry information over optical fiber lines under the control of computers. The combination of optics and computers represents the beginning of a revolution in communications technology. Other centers, including the Biotechnology Process Engineering Center at M.I.T., which conducts research on engineering to improve manufacturing processes in the biotechnology industry, are designed to focus on promising frontier technologies likely to transform some types of manufacturing in the near future.

The work of the NAE in support of engineering education in the United States was proceeding also along broader lines. In the early 1980s NAE member Jerrier A. Haddad, former vice president, technical personnel development, IBM Corporation, led a comprehensive NRC-based study that

Optical fibers thinner than a human hair can carry many times more information than copper wires for lower-cost telecommunications.

in 1985 resulted in a nine-volume analysis entitled *Engineering Education and Practice in the United States.* This series of reports pointed to the need for change in the universities and suggested ways of improving the quality of education and the methodology of teaching as well as the problems of expanding the interest of American students in graduate study.

NAE also played a part in stimulating engineering education in industry. In 1986 the Industry Advisory Board urged the NAE to step up to the problem of "engineer obsolescence" in a rapidly changing world. The result was *Focus on the Future: A National Action Plan for Career-Long Education for Engineers,* a report of a study chaired by NAE member Thomas L. Martin, Jr., president of the Illinois Institute of Technology. The report urged U.S. industry to recognize the long-term economic value of underwriting additional education for employees, noting that if it was true that many large companies were not doing as much as they could, then small companies had an even poorer record of supporting career education. In a "national action plan" the study team called on industry to invest in special courses geared to career-long training "in the use of new tools, processes, and systems that can help improve performance and productivity." They called on all parts of the engineering community, professional societies, industry, and the universities to form a coalition that would ensure the continued advance of career-long education.

Throughout the search for ways to improve engineering education, the NAE continued to find a staunch ally in the NSF and its director, NAE member Erich Bloch. Concerned both by the fact that U.S. students were not entering engineering schools in sufficient numbers and by the increasing prevalence of foreign graduate students in engineering, the NSF National Science Board, chaired by Roland Schmitt, in 1987 asked the Academy to help define what was really happening in graduate engineering education.

In response to this request, NAE initiated a study by the NRC Office of Scientific and Engineering Personnel. The study report, *Foreign and Foreign-Born Engineers in the United States: Infusing Talent, Raising Issues,* confirmed what many had observed—the skewing to foreign and foreign-born students was most pronounced at the graduate level. Not enough American students were entering graduate school; over fifty percent of those who obtained engineering doctorate degrees were foreign born and included a substantial number who said they would return to their country of origin. At

Erich Bloch

The NAE Industrial Mission to Sweden, shown with hosts at Saab-Scania in Linkoping in September 1985, was part of an exchange visit arranged by the NAE and the Royal Swedish Academy of Engineering Sciences.

the faculty level, about fifty percent of the younger engineering faculty were foreign citizens.

To ease the situation, the study group advised NSF that the engineering schools needed help from federal, state, and even industrial sources. On the federal and state levels, the experts proposed larger stipends and more fellowships for the first year or two of graduate study. NSF, they thought, might act as a clearinghouse to ensure access by university investigators to large facilities in government laboratories and in industry.

Encouraging International Collaboration

NAE also had long-term interests in the international engineering community. Following the Council's Decade III goal of encouraging international collaboration in engineering, White built on earlier international institutional activities to encourage consideration of the powerful forces acting on industry, the engineering enterprise, and education as a result of the globalization of technology and markets. In the mid-1970s, Foreign Secretary Hannay had expressed the idea that NAE should take a larger role in opening global communication among top engineers of the leading industrial nations and promoting international cooperation through the sharing of common technical problems and experiences. In 1978, as a response to visiting foreign engineers who wanted to adopt the U.S. Academy model to influence the policies of their own governments, Hannay proposed the establishment of a "convocation" of the world's engineering academies and similar organizations as a forum to achieve this objective.

The first International Convocation of Engineering Academies and Like Organizations, as it was then known, was hosted by the NAE in Washington, D.C., on October 31, 1978. Total attendance was ten, including representatives from four other academies—the Royal Swedish Academy of Engineering Sciences, the Australian Academy of Technological Sciences, the Mexican National Academy of Engineering, and the newly formed British Fellowship of Engineering. The success of this first convocation—the realization by the engineers of the different countries of the importance of technology in solving international societal problems—led to the establishment of the Council of Academies of Engineering and Technological Sciences (CAETS) and to a continuation of biennial convocations held around the world.

By 1983 the convocations had grown as seventy-five top engineers, representing sixteen countries, gathered in Stockholm, Sweden. Although the convocations were originally open only to nongovernment bodies, in the spirit of international cooperation invitations were extended to government observers from the Soviet Union, Yugoslavia, and the People's Republic of China.

White and Bechtel, and later Welch, agreed that the effectiveness of such an international body required the support of all leading technological nations on an equal basis. A concerted effort to encourage the formation of engineering academies in other countries found a welcome in Canada, Japan, India, and the Federal Republic of Germany.

As the CAETS idea gained momentum and the membership expanded, H. Guyford Stever, who was foreign secretary from 1984 to 1988, encouraged CAETS to engage more technological leaders in discussion of important policy issues. In 1987 he organized a discussion of technology and the global economy in a convocation held in Washington, D.C., under NAE auspices. The meeting drew some of the world's leading engineers and industrialists, who gathered to discuss state-of-the-art developments in manufacturing, new materials, information technology, and telecommunications.

The international outreach of the NAE was further extended by joint efforts with the NAS to engage engineering communities in Japan and China in a discussion of issues in technology and trade, innovation, manufacturing technology, and questions of access to scientific and engineering facilities.

In 1987 the National Science Board asked the NAE to examine issues related to international cooperation in engineering and to assess the growing interdependence of national engineering enterprises. Foreign Secretary Stever led the study. The report, *Strengthening U.S. Engineering Through International Cooperation: Some Recommendations for Action*, prompted Bechtel to observe that "being competitive in today's global context means being cooperative." Then, in 1988 the globalization of new technologies and the implications of a possible loss of engineering capabilities in critical fields were examined under the leadership of Thomas H. Lee of M.I.T. and NAE Foreign Secretary Gerald P. Dinneen in *Engineering as an International Enterprise.*

Gerald P. Dinneen

A New National Visibility

"The rise of NAE parallels the rise and importance of engineering and technology as a concern for government," said President Reagan's science and technology adviser Keyworth in testimony to a House subcommittee on the role of the Academies. The Council's goals were being met as NAE gained increased visibility through its public awareness program and the acceptance and use of its studies—all told more than forty-eight symposia, workshops, and other program activities were initiated between 1983 and 1989.

As the twenty-fifth anniversary of the NAE approached, two events symbolized the new vigor of the Academy. The first was the construction jointly with the NAS of the Arnold and Mabel Beckman Center of the National Academies of Sciences and Engineering in Irvine, California. The result of a gift of $20 million from NAE member Arnold O. Beckman, founder and chairman of Beckman Instruments, on land donated by The Irvine Company of California, the establishment of the center represented an important move for the Academies. Besides providing a western base for seminars, studies, and other activities, the center permitted the Academies greater access to the centers of excellence in the West and greater participa-

Arnold O. Beckman

tion in Academy programs by members who live there (twenty-five percent of the members of the two Academies reside in California alone). "The center is symbolic of how far the NAE has come," White observed. "It represents the first occasion in which both Academies shared equally in the building of an important facility."

Then, in 1988 the NAE received a request from the Charles Stark Draper Laboratory to establish the world's foremost award for engineering achievement with a monetary stipend of $350,000, approximately equivalent to the Nobel Prizes. Supported by a $4-million endowment, the Charles Stark Draper Prize, named after the M.I.T. pioneer of inertial guidance systems (a member of both NAE and NAS), was planned to be announced for the first time at the Academy's twenty-fifth annual meeting in October 1989. The award is to be given biennially to the engineer or engineers whose achievements have contributed most to human welfare and freedom.

The growing visibility of the National Academy of Engineering in national and world affairs has not gone unnoticed by the press or by Congress. In 1988 as many as fifty pieces of legislation called upon the Academy complex to undertake advisory studies; some fifteen of those explicitly called for participation of the National Academy of Engineering. As government agencies turned more often to the NAE, media attention to NAE's work increased severalfold, and word of its contributions to engineering began to reach the public. Symbolic of the growing recognition of engineers was the inclusion for the first time of "engineering" in the NSF's thirty-year-old annual statistical compilation. The bible of science information, formerly called *Science Indicators*, was now renamed *Science and Engineering Indicators*, a move made to reflect the expanded role of engineering in NSF.

Charles Stark Draper

Yet, the NAE leadership felt strongly that even this recognition of engineering and of the Academy's work was not enough. What was needed, Welch, Landau, and the Council agreed, was a more assertive role for the Academy. The Academy should speak out and lay before the political and decision-making public its views on directions and goals for the nation.

Building on a decade of work on international economic and technological competitiveness, the Academy put its efforts into assessing the relationships between technology and competitiveness and developing recommendations based on its findings. This resulted in the 1988 publication of *Technological Dimensions of International Competitiveness*, a widely distributed and well-received report with a national message, namely, that "U.S. industry must commit itself to offering world-class products and services at competitive costs."

The year 1988 was an election year, and NAE moved on other fronts to make its voice heard on the issue of competitiveness. The Council took on the task of preparing a brief statement on technology and competitiveness to be submitted to the administration of President George Bush as he took office in January 1989. "Technology and Competitiveness: A Statement of the Council of the National Academy of Engineering" outlined a concise program for a national technology policy made up of elements addressing macroeconomic policy, regulatory policy, education, and the joint government-industry role in supporting the nation's civil technology base. Drawing not only on the Council's diversified expertise but also on NAE's rich program experience, the statement emphasized that technology and science policy must be linked to economic and regulatory policymaking to enable the country to prosper and grow in a globally competitive environment. "The competitive threat to our country [is] of the utmost concern," the Council wrote to the new administration. "Nothing short of a bold and determined approach can restore the competitive position of the United States."

The NAE at Work in the Academy Complex

The NAE at Work in the Academy Complex

I n recent years, as the NAE has grown, the bulk of its work and most of its government advisory functions have been conducted through the joint operating arm of the NAS and NAE—the National Research Council. Indeed NAE's principal strength and influence on national affairs today is exercised through the NRC, which has grown into a $150-million-a-year enterprise. In any year, thirty percent of NAE members are active in NRC projects. More important, NAE plays a major role in determining which projects go forward and, through member participation in the work of the NRC, is influential in framing the issues to be addressed.

Each year some 200 studies are initiated, many of which come from government, while some are from private organizations and some are self-initiated. Subjects range from the routine to the cosmic and from the narrow perspective of a technical problem to broad policy recommendations. In recent years, the growth in the volume of work undertaken by the NRC has paralleled the growth of the NAE, doubling in the course of six years. This growth reflects the increased importance of engineering and science in advancing national goals and objectives.

The NRC receives eighty-five percent of its study support from the federal government; funding for independent Academy-initiated operations comes from a variety of private sources. These sources include the endowment income of the Academies and contributions from private foundations, corporations, members, and other individuals. The NRC scrupulously screens for bias all sources of funds as well as membership on committees and boards. Both the NAS and NAE presidents review the makeup of each committee and board to ensure balanced representation of engineers and scientists.

Almost every field in which engineering plays a role—space, aeronautics, transportation, manufacturing, electronics, services, environment, agriculture, health care, communications, infrastructure, and energy among others—is addressed by some unit of the NRC, often with extensive participation by NAE members.

Engineering and Technical Systems

The primary engineering unit of the NRC, the Commission on Engineering and Technical Systems (CETS), operates through twenty-one boards and standing committees. CETS is responsible for providing advice on a broad array of issues concerning technology and its applications. The commission's diverse activities reflect the growing complexity and sophistication of current technology as well as the close links among technology and social and economic concerns.

The aftermath of the space shuttle *Challenger* disaster in January 1986 provides one example of the ability of CETS and the NRC to carry out an important and complex study rapidly and reliably. The Academies were approached when the Presidential Commission on the Space Shuttle Challenger Accident, a twelve-member team appointed by President Reagan to investigate the explosion and recommend measures to ensure the safety of future space shuttle flights, suggested that NASA arrange for an independent evaluation of the redesign of the shuttle's solid rocket booster. NASA turned to the Academies to do the evaluation.

A weakness in the original design of this booster had been pinpointed as the cause of the *Challenger* explosion. The urgent need to redesign the solid rocket booster dictated a need for a speedy yet thorough response. A select group of experts, including several NAE members, was empaneled under the chairmanship of H. Guyford Stever to address NASA's concerns. The committee worked virtually continuously for two and one-half years probing every step in the design, test, and manufacture of the booster. Briefings for NASA were held once a month; in all, eight letter reports were

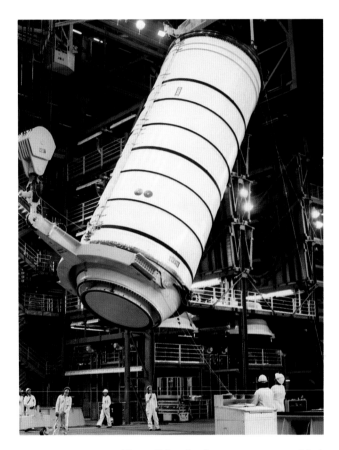

The solid rocket boosters are assembled at the Kennedy Space Center before the first orbital flight test of the space shuttle *Columbia* in 1979.

Over the Cape Verde Islands, the interweaving of oppositely curving wind currents after passage around an island demonstrates the Von Karman vortex.

sent to NASA administrator James C. Fletcher, himself an NAE member, with recommendations to guide preparations for the return of the shuttle to flight.

The committee's effectiveness in its oversight role was evident to the nation in the successful flight of the shuttle *Discovery* on September 29, 1988. Stever was awarded the Distinguished Public Service Medal, NASA's highest award given to a civilian; the members of the committee and staff were awarded the Public Service Medal; and the U.S. Senate passed a resolution of appreciation.

Physical Sciences, Mathematics, and Resources

The second NRC division with a significant engineering content is the Commission on Physical Sciences, Mathematics, and Resources (CPSMR). This commission ambitiously defines its goal as "ensuring the health and progress of the physical and chemical sciences, the sciences of the atmo-

sphere, the oceans, the earth and its resources, the space and natural plane-
tary sciences and mathematics including computer science and statistics." In
each case, its concerns range from basic science and research to applications
and implications for national policy.

Organized into approximately 240 boards and committees with
more than 2,300 members, all overseen by twenty-two commission members, CPSMR alone completed fifty-four reports in 1988. Study subjects var-
ied from an examination of space science in the twenty-first century to an
assessment of the competitive position of photonics, a project initiated by
NAE. This commission has also examined such timely concerns as the perception and communication of risk and the advanced technologies that are
likely to affect the security of the United States. CPSMR committees and
boards have worked with the Department of Defense in long-range planning for the Navy, with NASA for the space program beyond the year 2000,
with the National Park Service on the research necessary to manage national
parks in the next century, and with the Department of the Interior on future
directions in water resource management.

CPSMR boards have examined the prospects for global climate
change, conducted studies of the competitive status of the U.S.computer
industry, and blueprinted future research opportunities in chemical engineering. From groundwater contamination to the management of toxic sub-
stances in the environment, the commission continues to be responsive to
requests for advice from the government.

When called on to do so, CPSMR can and does respond quickly.
Shortly after the news broke of the accident at Chernobyl in the Soviet Union,
the U.S. government began to raise concerns about the safety of U.S. nuclear
plants. Energy Secretary John Herrington moved swiftly, asking the NAE
and the NAS to evaluate safety and technical issues raised by the accident in
relation to safety in U.S. nuclear facilities.

To undertake the study, Press and White alerted the two engineering-
oriented NRC commissions—CETS and CPSMR. The commissions quickly
organized a committee scrutinized by Press and White for balance and expertise. Because of his experience at the Windscale nuclear plant in Britain—a
nuclear plant similar to Chernobyl—an expert was brought in from England.

The committee's findings were delivered in March 1987, less than one year after the Chernobyl disaster. The findings suggested that, among other things, the well-publicized reactors at the Savannah River plant were operating at power levels that posed the risk of significant core damage in the event of a severe loss of coolant. Earlier DOE had analyzed the problem at Savannah River and ordered a twenty-six percent reduction in power, but the committee found that reduction insufficient and advised DOE to immediately establish "an aggressive course of action to ensure the safety of the reactors in a severe loss of coolant accident."

Transportation Research

Engineering is the central focus of the largest and oldest single entity associated with the NRC, the Transportation Research Board (TRB) with over 270 standing committees and study panels dealing with all aspects of transportation including operations, economics, construction, and new technology. When the board was formed in 1920, its main concerns were with building the new roads resulting from the passage of the first Federal-aid Highway Act passed in 1916. By 1989 the board's concerns had broadened to include all modes of transportation—surface, air, and water. Frequently TRB is called on to study and make recommendations on safety-related matters, including the national fifty-five miles per hour speed limit, the safety of the new larger and heavier trucks, and school bus safety. It also addresses questions of air carrier deregulation and containerized intermodal freight movement.

The $150-million Strategic Highway Research Program was organized in 1986 as a result of a TRB study project. The main concern of this program, organized separately from the TRB, is the physical preservation of transportation infrastructure including highway and runway pavements and bridges. Currently TRB is gearing up for a stronger involvement in the assessment of unfavorable environmental impacts of transportation, including problems of air quality and problems associated with alternative transportation fuels.

Public Policy

Over the course of the past twenty-five years, steps have been taken by NAS and NAE to sponsor activities jointly wherever they made obvious sense. In 1981 the twenty-year-old Committee on Science and Public Policy, known

Although the total length of all roads has remained unchanged over the past sixty years, increased vehicle use has focused concern on the physical preservation of the highway infrastructure.

familiarly by the acronym COSPUP, (an NAS committee formed in 1961 to focus on public policy dimensions of scientific advances) took on an "E" for engineering to become COSEPUP. This move recognized that engineering had become an integral part of the Academies' structure and that engineering issues were a significant contributor to institutional recommendations on public policy.

Today COSEPUP has become an important nongovernmental body providing advice in the matter of science and technology and their interaction with society. It has provided special briefings on timely scientific and technological subjects for the Office of Science and Technology Policy in the White House, the NSF, and for other federal agencies. COSEPUP has published landmark reports on issues surrounding technology and employment and on the peer review process for allocation of funding for research projects. Currently, COSEPUP is examining the potential impact of global warming, the ethical norms of scientific conduct, and the effectiveness of government policies in support of this country's technological capability.

A striking example of the impact of COSEPUP's work is the effect of its 1987 report, *Balancing the National Interest: U.S. National Security Export Controls and Global Economic Competition.* The report was written by a group of industrialists, former defense and intelligence officials, academics, lawyers, and economists chaired by NAE member Lew Allen, Jr., director of the Jet Propulsion Laboratory of the California Institute of Technology, former chief of staff for the Air Force, and a former director of the National Security Agency. The committee concluded that the government's efforts to crack down through the export control laws on the diversion of technology to the Soviet Union and other Communist bloc countries had seriously impeded U.S. trade in high-technology products while making an unclear and variable contribution to national security. Allen and his panel recommended severe reductions in the list of technologies protected by the United States and its allies. Equipment such as computer chips and personal computers, the group pointed out, could no longer be kept locked at home by export controls because both the technology and the products easily crossed national boundaries.

Once issued, the report raised a furor among some senior defense officials who saw it as an attack on accepted policy. Later, however, it was cited as a major contribution to a dialogue that has led to the removal of certain export restrictions and to improvement of the U.S. position in export control collaboration with NATO allies and other friendly nations.

The Academy complex has also directed its attention to encouraging new lines of cooperation among government, academia, and private industry. Examples of this new outward focus are two joint activities of the Academies and the IOM—the Government-University-Industry Research Roundtable (GUIRR) and the Academy Industry Program (AIP).

GUIRR comprises a broad range of professionals from both the public and private sectors. It is a forum where leaders of the research enterprise gather on a regular basis and in a structured environment to address issues affecting the strength and vitality of the nation's research function. While steering clear of making specific recommendations, it develops options and provides a neutral setting in which both short- and long-term priorities can be discussed.

The AIP is another vehicle for developing effective communication between the Academies and industry. Founded in 1983, AIP provides a two-way channel of communication between the NRC and industry, furthering effective dissemination of NRC reports to appropriate people in industry and providing an efficient means by which industry views can be brought to the attention of the Research Council's leadership and staff. The AIP also provides financial support for those institutionally initiated studies where government funding may be inappropriate or unavailable. In its first half-decade, the AIP has developed a membership of more than seventy of the world's leading companies and has sponsored symposia and studies on matters ranging from genetic engineering to international economics.

As 1989 unfolded, the NAE took still another important step, one targeted to meet the Academy goal of becoming a major force for advancing engineering and technology in the United States. It joined with the National Academy of Sciences and the Institute of Medicine in moving toward more vigorous, assertive participation in setting national goals. The essence of this participation was to provide President Bush and the incoming administration with a series of "white papers" on four critical issues, important to the technological and scientific future of the nation and the world.

In these white papers, the Academies and IOM spoke out on the

The elevated concentration of greenhouse gases produced to date will persist for many centuries and may slowly change the climate of the earth.

need for strengthening the role of the president's science and technology adviser. They confronted head-on the development of policies and actions that the country must address to forestall and to adjust to the threatening change in the global environment and to control the spread of AIDS. Jointly the Academies and IOM spelled out the need for the nation to take a clear and unambiguous position on space policy and programs in order to restore U.S. leadership in space. This historic move by the Academies and the Institute of Medicine—never before had they spoken on their own initiative with a single voice on major policy issues—will be, it is hoped, the harbinger of a new and productive era for the NAE and the Academy complex.

Changing Horizons

Robert M. White
President, National Academy of Engineering

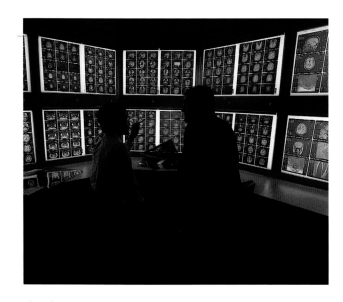

Combining computer and x-ray technology, computerized axial tomography, or CAT scanning, enables physicians to diagnose tumors and internal injuries without exploratory surgery.

New engineering and technological horizons continue to unfold as the National Academy of Engineering enters its second quarter century. We cannot predict the future shape of engineering, but if history is any guide, we can expect dramatic and unpredictable technological changes—the fruits of creative minds in both science and engineering.

We look back on a quarter century in which society has been transformed by science, engineering, and technology. The changes have been momentous. The microprocessor is ubiquitous in its effects on almost all aspects of human existence in industrially developed societies. It has been the seminal invention of the information age. In manufacturing, it has revolutionized the management and control of production processes. The personal computer has transformed office, home, and business life. For the individual it has opened new dimensions in home entertainment, retail shopping, and automatic banking.

Computer-aided design and manufacturing (CAD/CAM) have transformed engineering design and manufacturing processes. Medical diagnostic imaging, such as computerized axial tomography (CAT scan) and magnetic resonance imaging, has transformed the field of medical diagnosis. The laser, like the microprocessor, has revolutionized approaches in such disparate fields as surgery and materials processing, and it has opened the field of optical communications.

More than 8 million miles from Earth, the *Voyager 2* spacecraft sends back close-ups of Saturn and its ring system, August 1981.

The achievements of space technology are no less remarkable. Indeed, the landing of men on the moon is the crowning engineering achievement of modern times. By comparison, the operational use of earth-orbiting satellites is commonplace, yet it has come to fruition only in the past twenty-five years. Satellites in earth orbit now provide worldwide instantaneous communications to the most remote areas of the world and bring us television programming from every nation. They now routinely monitor global weather conditions and provide storm warnings that have become indispensable in protecting life and property from hurricanes and tornadoes. Satellites explore the solar system and have transformed our understanding of the universe. By providing verification of arms control agreements and assurance against surprise attack, surveillance satellites have been, and continue to be, keys to global peace-keeping.

Engineering made it possible to design composite materials to meet specific requirements for strength, flexibility, and corrosion resistance. Now

With a capacity of 300 to 450 passengers and range of more than 6,000 miles, wide-body jumbo jets carry passengers more cost-effectively than smaller planes.

routinely used in mobile and stationary applications, these materials have enabled such feats as the historic flight of the aircraft *Voyager* around the world without refueling.

Engineering has also brought about a revolution in mass air transportation, most recently through the development of wide-body jets wedded to high-bypass turbofan engines. Agricultural technology has transformed numerous developing nations from net importers to net exporters of foods. Genetically engineered products in biotechnology have transformed the way we think about development and production of pharmaceuticals and new strains of plant and animal life that will have profound influence on agriculture. These examples give further assurance that in the next twenty-five years, engineering will be as creative as in the past twenty-five years and that the world will be transformed once again through innovative technological achievement.

However, although we cannot predict specific engineering achievements, we can predict, with some confidence, the global forces that will impinge on the engineering and technological enterprise in the next quarter century. The principal challenge to the Academy will be to assist in channeling engineering and technology to respond to these forces. What are some of these forces? Perhaps the most encompassing is the increasing interdependence among nations in a global economy. Our task will be to show the ways in which the United States can prosper in the emerging polycentric world in which economic and technological power and excellence are widely distributed among nations.

Our national vision has too often been confined to achieving our objectives within our national borders, but this pattern is changing. The United States, despite its economic and military strength, is no longer self-sufficient. We are increasingly dependent for our finance, resources, technology, and science on the actions of other nations throughout the world. The forces of globalization and interdependence raise issues about how the United States can maintain its technological competitiveness. In the process we will need to confront the difficult issue of how the national interest can best be served by balancing national and corporate sovereignty and competitiveness.

Globalization brings with it not only economic and technological dilemmas but also those related to the environment and energy. We are entering a period of accelerating deterioration of the global environment. The processes of deterioration have been under way for a century as industrial and agricultural technology has diffused to advance standards of living throughout the world. In the future, humanity will need to address the preservation of the habitability of large areas of the world while providing the food and energy supplies needed for its well-being. Engineering and technology will need to offer solutions. Environmental deterioration is now global in scope. Causes and consequences are distributed widely and unevenly among many nations. The issue is manifest in the projections of a warming of the global climate, a result of increasing concentrations of "greenhouse" gases such as carbon dioxide.

But climate warming is only one global environmental phenomenon. Stratospheric ozone is thought to be undergoing depletion; tropical forests are being destroyed; species extinction is accelerating; and the effects of acid deposition on lake ecology are well documented. The management of technology, largely in the absence of knowledge of adverse consequences, has at least in part been responsible for some of the environmental deterioration. But the planet's environmental condition is directly related to the most fundamental activities of humanity: the production of food and energy and the aspirations for economic development among the poorer countries of the world. The wise application of innovative engineering and technology represents a major challenge to the world engineering community and to this Academy. There will be pressing need for environmentally benign production and use of energy. Greater energy efficiency and the development of publicly acceptable sources of nonfossil energy such as nuclear and solar will be required.

Among the forces with which engineering will have to contend are those that result from rising expectations and demand for a more livable society. Both surface and air transportation systems are approaching gridlock. The public demand for technologically safe industrial systems will need to be met. The antitechnology reaction that occurs in public opinion when industrial operations result in catastrophic events like Bhopal, Three Mile Island, and Prince William Sound can be reversed only if there is a new commitment to engineering for public safety, whether in nuclear power, chemical plants, or the disposal of hazardous wastes.

Much as the global economy will change relations among nations, the change in the business environment will alter the role of the individual engineer. As individual companies and industries become more dependent on the application of engineering and the rapid adoption of technological innovation in the production of competitive products and services, engineers will become the central switching points in companies. The engineer will increasingly be the key to bridging different fields of knowledge—for example, between scientific discovery and its conversion into commercial products and between product design and engineering, and production and marketing. The engineer's role will become even more important as the relationship of engineering to science becomes increasingly blurred and the time for conversion from scientific discovery to engineering design and production shrinks.

The implication of these changing forces for engineering education is profound. Engineering education has been altered over the years as universities have responded to changing industrial needs for engineering talent. But as technological developments appear with greater rapidity, and as greater specialization is required, engineering education will face a dilemma. The university engineering education system will need to provide an engineering education of continued high quality but of greater breadth. The daunting task will be made more difficult by the need for new facilities and the rebuilding of engineering faculties. And traditional disciplines of engineering will have to prosper even while new areas of engineering specialization arise. How we will do this represents a clear challenge to academia, industry, and government.

How will public policies be shaped to respond to these forces? I believe that the National Academy of Engineering is uniquely positioned to play an important role. We have become a strong voice for engineering and technology, and this voice will need to be further strengthened. We must continue to nominate and elect to our Academy individuals with great achievements in advancing engineering and technology. Only in this way can we truly represent the nation's engineering leadership and remain credible as a source of advice for our government.

The Academy has taken on a more assertive role in the past few years. We have spoken out on a range of topics: technology and economic growth; the need for a new national technology policy; a responsible space policy; the establishment of processes for better budgetary allocation of funds for science and technology; and the need for high-level science and technology advice within the federal government.

We have adopted this more assertive role in close collaboration with the National Academy of Sciences and the Institute of Medicine with whom we share the congressional charter for advising the federal government on matters of science and engineering and medicine. During the past twenty-five years, we have developed an effective working relationship with our partners in the Academy complex.

We have also continued our close relationship with many of the professional engineering societies representing the broader engineering community, as well as formed new relationships with foreign engineering communities through collaborative efforts with other academies of engineering. The formation and growth of the international Council of Academies of Engineering and Technological Sciences have provided an important forum bringing together technological leaders from many nations. In the next twenty-five years we will need to expand and further cement these relationships, for they will be needed if we are to discharge our larger obligation to serve our nation and the world. This we will do through the exercise of the engineering and technological leadership represented in the members of this Academy.

Founding members attending the first
annual meeting of the National Academy
of Engineering, April 27–29, 1965.
From left to right, standing: Ernst Weber,
Michael L. Haider, Charles A. Thomas,
William L. Everitt, Julius A. Stratton,
Frederick E. Terman, Thomas K. Sherwood,
Clark B. Millikan, James N. Landis,
Hendrick W. Bodé, and Nathan M. Newmark.
Seated: Thomas C. Kavanagh, Augustus B. Kinzel,
and Eric A. Walker, with first NAE Secretary
Harold K. Work.

NAE Members and Foreign Associates

As of July 1, 1989

Members

by year of election

1964

Bodé, Hendrik W.†
Cisler, Walker L. (C)
Dryden, Hugh L.†
Engstrom, Elmer W. (C)†
Everitt, William L.†
Gaudin, Antoine M. (C)†
Haider, Michael L. (C)†
Holbrook, George E. (C)†
Hollomon, J. Herbert (C)†
Kavanagh, Thomas C. (T)†
Kinzel, Augustus B. (P, C)†
Landis, James N.†
Linder, Clarence H. (P, VP, C)
Millikan, Clark B.†
Newmark, Nathan M. (C)†
Pickering, William H.
Ramo, Simon (C)
Raymond, Arthur E.
Sherwood, Thomas K.†
Stratton, Julius A. (C)
Suits, C. G.
Terman, Frederick E.†
Thomas, Charles A. (C)†

LEGEND

(P) President
(C) Councillor
(Ch) Chairman
(VP) Vice President
(HS) Home Secretary
(FS) Foreign Secretary
(AP) Acting President
(T) Treasurer
(S) Secretary
† Deceased

Walker, Eric A. (P, VP, C)
Weber, Ernst (C)

1965

Ammann, Othmar H.†
Bainer, Roy
Barr, Harry F.
Bisplinghoff, Raymond L. (C)†
Brown, George H.†
Brown, Gordon S. (C)
Chadwick, Wallace L.
Draper, Charles Stark†
Emmons, Howard W.
Fetters, Karl L.
Folsom, Richard G. (C)
Gibbs, William F.†
Gilbreth, Lillian M.†
Gilliland, Edwin R.†
Ginzton, Edward L. (C)
Haggerty, Patrick E. (C)†
Heald, Henry T.†
Heinemann, Edward H.
Hewlett, William R.
Hoff, Nicholas J.
Holloway, Frederic A. L. (T, C)
Housner, George W.
Johnson, Clarence L.
Land, Edwin H.
Liepmann, Hans W.
Link, Edwin A.†
McKeen, John E.†
McLean, William B.†
Mettler, Ruben F.
Monteith, Alexander C.†
Peck, Ralph B.
Pierce, John R. (C)
Prager, William†
Puckett, Allen E.
Root, L. Eugene (C)
Sinclair, Donald B.†
Skilling, John B.
Smith, Levering

Sporn, Philip†
Starr, Chauncey (VP, C)
Stever, H. Guyford (FS, C)
Todd, Frederick H.
Truxal, John G.
Whinnery, John R.
Wolman, Abel†
Zworykin, Vladimir Kosma†

1966

Allen, H. Julian†
Beranek, Leo L. (C)
Berry, Donald S.
Busignies, Henri (C)†
Casagrande, Arthur†
Chilton, Thomas H.†
David, Edward E., Jr. (C)
Edgerton, Harold E.
Fisk, James B.†
Fubini, Eugene G. (C)
Hawkins, Willis M.
Hibbard, Walter R., Jr. (C)
Keil, Alfred A. H.
Kompfner, Rudolph†
Landsberg, Helmut E.†
Lewis, Warren K.†
McCune, Francis K.
Mindlin, Raymond D.†
Oliver, Bernard M.
Piore, E. R.
Prutton, Carl F.†
Rajchman, Jan A.†
Rouse, Hunter
Simpson, John W.
Suomi, Verner E.
Villard, Oswald G., Jr.
Wiesner, Jerome B.

1967

Ackermann, William C. (C)†
Adler, Robert

Amdahl, Gene M.
Austin, James B.†
Bachman, Walter C.
Baker, Robert A., Sr.†
Beckman, Arnold O.
Benedict, Manson
Biot, Maurice A.†
Boundy, Ray H.
Boyd, James†
Brown, Harold
Cassidy, William F.
Chesebrough, Harry E.
Chodorow, Marvin
Cleary, Edward J.†
Cohen, Karl P.
Davis, Frank W.
Davis, Harmer E.
Deere, Don U.
Dessauer, John H. (C)
Douglas, Donald W.†
Douglas, Walter S.†
Drucker, Daniel C.
Eckert, J. Presper
Elston, Charles W.
Fair, Gordon M.†
Fenske, Merrell R.†
Ferri, Antonio†
Field, Lester M.
Flax, Alexander H. (HS)
Fontana, Mars G.†
Forrester, Jay W.
Frey, Donald N. (C)
Furnas, Clifford C.†
Glennan, T. Keith (C)
Goland, Martin (C)
Goldmark, Peter C.†
Gotaas, Harold B.†
Hait, James M.
Hawkins, George A.†
Herwald, S. W.
Hillier, James (C)
Hollis, Mark D.
Holloway, Marshall G.

Hunsaker, Jerome C.†
Ippen, Arthur T.†
Jordan, Edward C.
Kaman, Charles H.
Kiely, John R.
Kilby, Jack S.
Killian, James R., Jr.†
Kirkbride, Chalmer G.
Kyle, John M., Jr.†
Lederer, Jerome F.
Lewis, W. Deming (C)†
Lin, T. Y.
Lindvall, Frederick C.†
Ling, Donald P.†
Loughlin, Bernard D.†
MacMillan, Douglas C.
Maiman, Theodore H.
Marshall, W. Robert†
Mauchly, John†
McAfee, Jerry
McDonnell, James S.†
Morton, Jack A.†
Mueller, George E.
Palladino, Nunzio J.
Pettit, Joseph M. (C)†
Pratt, Perry W.†
Rickover, Hyman G.†
Roddis, Louis H., Jr.
Schairer, George S.
Schriever, Bernard A.
Sheets, Herman E.
Shoupp, William E. (AP, VP)†
Siess, Chester P.
Silverstein, Abe
Smith, Mark K.
Solomon, George E.
Sparks, William J.†
Squires, Lombard
Tatlow, Richard H., III
Tedesko, Anton
von Braun, Wernher†
Wells, Edward C.†
Wheaton, Elmer P.

Wilbur, Lyman D.
Wilson, Stanley D.†
Wood, Carlos C.
Young, James F.†

1968

Avila, Charles F.
Barlow, Edward J.
Bell, Milo C.
Brooks, Harvey
Burnham, Donald C.
Burriss, Stanley W.†
Clough, Ray W.
Collins, Arthur A.†
Cross, Ralph E.
Getting, Ivan A.
Gilruth, Robert R.
Haddad, Jerrier A.
Hafstad, Lawrence R.
Hall, William J.
Jenks, Stephen M.†
Johnson, Wilfrid E.†
Johnson, Woodrow E.
Katz, Donald L.†
Keith, Percival C.†
Kelly, Clarence F.†
Logan, John A.†
Lustman, Benjamin
MacDonnell, W. D.
McKay, Kenneth G. (C)
Mentzer, William C.†
Miller, Otto N.†
Miller, Rene H.
Murphy, Eugene F.
Nichols, Kenneth D.
Noble, Daniel E.†
Old, Bruce S. (FS)
Osborn, Elburt F.
Paige, Hilliard W.
Pearson, Gerald L.†
Pennell, Maynard L.
Rechtin, Eberhardt
Ross, Philip N.
Rowand, Will H.
Rutledge, Philip C.
Seamans, Robert C., Jr. (P, C)
Sears, William R.
Severud, Fred N.
Shaw, Milton C.
Sikorsky, Igor I.†
Silver, Samuel†
Smith, Wilbur S.
Watkins, Dean A.
Wessenauer, G. O.

White, Robert M. (P, C)
Wilhelm, Richard H.†

1969

Alvarez, Luis W.†
Bacon, Vinton W.
Bauer, Robert F.
Bird, R. Byron
Blume, John A.
Bromberg, Robert
Brumer, Milton
Cairns, Robert W. (C)†
Chenea, Paul F. (C)
Cohn, Nathan
DeLauer, Richard D.
Donovan, Allen F.
Fink, Donald G.
Fisher, Harold W.
Foster, John S., Jr.
Grosh, Richard J.
Gunness, Robert C. (C)
Jacobs, J. Donovan
Jacobs, John E.
Jaffee, Robert I.
Jones, Thomas F.†
Kessler, George W.†
Knowles, Hugh S.†
Latham, Allen, Jr.
Lawroski, Stephen
Ludwig, Harvey F.
Malozemoff, Plato
McKee, Jack E.†
McLucas, John L. (C)
McMillan, Brockway
Molnar, Julius P.†
Noyce, Robert N.
O'Brien, Morrough P.†
Parker, Earl R.
Perkins, Courtland D. (P, C)
Peters, Max S.
Reed, Charles E.
Richart, Frank E., Jr.
Shepherd, William G.
Spaght, Monroe E.
Swearingen, John E.
Teal, Gordon K.
Waynick, Arthur H.†
Wenk, Edward, Jr. (C)

1970

Amundson, Neal R.
Arnold, Philip M.
Ashley, Holt (C)

Baxter, Samuel S.†
Bellport, Bernard P.
Bowman, Robert A.†
Bryson, Arthur E., Jr. (C)
Busemann, Adolf†
Bush, Spencer H.
Chambers, Carl C.†
Clauser, Francis H. (C)
Cole, Edward N. (T)†
Craven, John P.
Cullum, A. Earl, Jr.†
Cutler, C. Chapin
Davis, W. Kenneth (VP, C)
Dickieson, Alton C.
Eckert, Ernst R. G.
Evans, Bob O.
Faget, Maxime A.
Fletcher, James C. (C)
Geyer, John C.
Gloyna, Earnest F. (C)
Hall, Albert C.
Huggins, William H.
Johnson, Wendell E.†
Ketchledge, Raymond W.†
Kraft, Christopher C., Jr.
Lehan, Frank W.
Leverenz, Humboldt W.
Low, George M. (C)†
Macdonald, J. Ross (C)
McKetta, John J., Jr.
McMaster, Robert C.†
Neumann, Gerhard
Perkins, Kendall†
Perry, William J.
Quate, Calvin F.
Rader, Louis T.
Richards, Robert B.†
Robinson, Denis M.
Rohlich, Gerard A.†
Rosenberg, Paul
Schwartzwalder, Karl†
Seed, H. Bolton†
Shepherd, Mark, Jr.
Smullin, Louis D.
Souders, Mott, Jr.†
Wagner, Harvey A.
Wheelon, Albert D.
Winter, George†

1971

Baird, Jack A.†
Blasingame, B. Paul
Bowhill, Sidney A.
Currie, Malcolm R.

Douma, Jacob H.
Eliassen, Rolf
Elmendorf, Charles H., III
Ference, Michael, Jr.
Frosch, Robert A.
Frye, John C.†
Gornowski, Edward J.†
Gould, Roy W.
Harper, John D.†
Heffner, Hubert†
Jonsson, J. Erik
Lees, Lester†
Lewis, David S., Jr.
Linvill, John G.
Loewy, Robert G.
Ludwig, John H.
Martin, Thomas L., Jr.
Mechlin, George F.
Packard, David
Phillips, Samuel C. (C)
Phillips, Thomas L.
Pigford, Robert L.†
Reed, Eugene D.
Shea, Joseph F.
Smelt, Ronald

1972

Babb, Albert L.
Bardeen, John
Beedle, Lynn S.
Cohen, Morris
Eggers, Alfred J., Jr.
Johnson, James R.
Kraus, John D.
Lambe, T. William
Landau, Ralph (VP, C)
Sliepcevich, Cedomir M.
Tanenbaum, Morris (C)

1973

Bailey, Stuart L.†
Ballhaus, William F., Sr. (C)
Banks, Harvey O.
Brooks, Norman H.
Brown, Burton P.
Buchsbaum, Solomon J. (C)
Caldwell, Joseph M.†
Cannon, Robert H., Jr. (C)
Caplan, John D.
Cermak, Jack E.
Charyk, Joseph V.
Chow, Ven Te†
Clarke, Frederick J.

Cortright, Edgar M.
Dacey, George C.
Davenport, Lee L.
Fano, Robert M.
Ferguson, Phil M.†
Fine, Morris E.
Gerwick, Ben C., Jr.
Gifford, Richard P.†
Ginsburg, Charles P.
Gould, William R.
Hedefine, Alfred†
Hognestad, Eivind
Hollister, Solomon C.†
Holonyak, Nick, Jr.
Hopper, Grace M.
Hudson, Donald E.
Humphrey, Arthur E.
Johnson, H. Richard
Jones, Robert T.
Kennedy, John F.
Khan, Fazlur R.†
Larson, Clarence E.
Lawler, Joseph C.†
Leps, Thomas M.
Mann, Robert W.
Mauch, Hans A.†
McCarthy, Gerald T.
McGauhey, Percy H.†
Metzler, Dwight F.
Miller, Stewart E.
Myers, Phillip S.
Nagel, Theodore J.†
Newman, Joseph H.
Okun, Daniel A.
Paine, Thomas O.
Parks, Robert J.
Peterson, Allen M.
Pikarsky, Milton†
Potter, David S.
Rand, William B. W.†
Rees, Eberhard F. M.
Rosen, Harold A.
Rosenbaum, Joe B.†
Rosenblith, Walter A.
Ross, Ian M.
Roy, Rustum
Rummel, Robert W.
Schade, Henry A.
Siegman, Anthony E.
Sparks, Morgan
Starbird, Alfred D.†
Sutherland, Ivan E.
Tribus, Myron
Turner, Howard S.
Van Valkenburg, M. E.

Wagner, Aubrey J.
Zadeh, Lotfi A.

1974

Adcock, Willis A.
Agnew, William G.
Arnold, Wm. Howard
Atwood, J. Leland
Auerbach, Isaac L.
Barnes, Howard C.
Barrow, Thomas D.
Baruch, Jordan J.
Battin, Richard H.
Bauer, Benjamin B.†
Bergen, William B.†
Bitzer, Donald L.
Boyle, Willard S.
Branscomb, Lewis M.
Bucy, J. Fred
Bueche, Arthur M. (C)†
Carlson, Roy W.
Carrier, George F.
Casagrande, Leo
Chestnut, Harold
Churchill, Stuart W.
Culler, Floyd L.
Drake, Robert M., Jr.
Dresselhaus, Mildred S. (C)
Eisenberg, Phillip†
Elms, James C.
Everett, James L., III
Fair, James R.
Felker, Jean H.
Field, A. J.
Fink, Daniel J.
Flawn, Peter T.
Fucik, E. Montford
Gaden, Elmer L., Jr.
Gagnebin, Albert P.
Gavin, Joseph G., Jr.
Gibbons, James F.
Haensel, Vladimir
Hamming, Kenneth W.
Hancock, John C.
Haney, Paul D.
Hannay, N. Bruce (FS)
Hanratty, Thomas J.
Harleman, Donald R. F.
Hazen, Richard
Hedrick, Ira G.
Hirth, John P.
Hocott, Claude R.
Hottel, Hoyt C.
Hougen, Olaf A.†

Levy, Salomon
Linden, Henry R.
Little, C. Gordon
Lovelace, Alan M.
Lowe, John, III
Manly, William D.
Marble, Frank E.
Matsuda, Fujio
Moll, John L.
Mulligan, James H., Jr. (S)
Myers, Dale D.
Okrent, David
Parme, Alfred L.
Pederson, Donald O.
Pellini, William S.†
Peterson, Dean F.†
Plunkett, Robert
Scott, Ronald F.
Shapiro, Ascher H.
Sjoberg, Sigurd A.
Soderberg, C. Richard†
Taylor, John J.
Tenenbaum, Michael (C)
Tillinghast, John A.
Westwater, James W.
Whitman, Walter G.†
Wilson, Thornton A.
Zinn, Walter H.

1975

Ancker-Johnson, Betsy
Anderson, Arthur G.
Aris, Rutherford
Atkin, Rupert L.
Baker, W. O.
Beard, Leo R.
Bechtel, Stephen D., Jr. (Ch, C)
Binger, Wilson V.
Bobeck, Andrew H.
Bogdanoff, John L.
Boley, Bruno A.
Brian, P. L. Thibaut
Brown, Alfred E.
Brown, J. H. U.
Burnett, James R.
Chapman, Dean R.
Charpie, Robert A. (C)
Coffin, Louis F., Jr.
Cohen, Edward
Dahlstrom, Donald A.
Daily, James W.
Darlington, Sidney
Davenport, Wilbur B., Jr.
Debus, Kurt H.†

Den Hartog, Jacob P.†
Dietrich, Joseph R.†
Dillard, Joseph K.†
Dinneen, Gerald P. (FS, C)
Eldred, Kenneth McK.
Elliott, John F.
Evans, Ersel A.
Fadum, Ralph E.
Friedlander, Sheldon K.
Giaever, Ivar
Gilman, John J.
Gomory, Ralph E. (C)
Gordon, William E.
Granger, John V. N.
Gray, Paul E. (C)
Harris, Cyril M.
Hawkins, W. Lincoln
Hayes, Thomas J., III
Hayes, Wallace D.
Hornbeck, John A.†
Hrones, John A.
Huebner, George J., Jr.
Jacobsen, Lydik S.†
Jordan, Richard C.
Kingery, W. David
Kuh, Ernest S.
Lee, Erastus H.
Lee, Thomas H.
Liebowitz, Harold (HS)
Mason, Edward A. (C)
Merchant, M. Eugene
Michael, Harold L.
Millar, Gordon H.
Milliken, Frank R.
Mueller, Erwin W.†
Oblad, Alex G.
O'Neill, Russell R.
Osterberg, Jorj O.
Pask, Joseph A.
Petrone, Rocco A.
Reese, Lymon C.
Reichl, Eric H.
Robertson, Leslie E.
Rohsenow, Warren M.
Rose, Albert
Schwan, Herman P.
Sinfelt, John H.
Smith, Joe M.
Smith, Robert L.
Sternberg, Eli†
Thon, J. George†
Tien, Ping King
Timmerhaus, Klaus D.
Townsend, John W., Jr.
Weinberg, Alvin M.

Wenzel, James G.
White, David C.
Whitman, Robert V.
Wiegel, Robert L.
Wilke, Charles R.
Willenbrock, F. Karl (C)
Woodson, Herbert H.

1976

Abramson, H. Norman (C)
Agnew, Harold M.
Allen, Clarence R.
Ang, Alfredo H-S.
Beattie, Horace S.
Berg, Daniel (C)
Blickwede, Donald J.
Breen, John E.
Brinckerhoff, Charles M.†
Brooks, Frederick P., Jr.
Broughton, Donald B.†
Budiansky, Bernard
Burke, Joseph E.
Camras, Marvin
Clewell, Dayton H.
Cole, Julian D.
Coltman, John W.
Cooper, Franklin S.
Corbato, Fernando J.
Davis, Ruth M.
DeMaria, Anthony J.
Dyer, Ira
Edlund, Milton C.
Elkins, Lloyd E.
Elliott, Martin A.†
Engelbrecht, Richard S.
Estes, Elliott M.†
Feinstein, Joseph
Fenves, Steven J.
Field, Michael
Flemings, Merton C.
Fogarty, Charles F.†
Fox, Gerard F.
Freudenthal, Alfred M.†
Fu, King-Sun†
Fuerstenau, Douglas W.
Fuhrman, Robert A.
Golomb, Solomon W.
Goodenough, John B.
Gooding, Robert C.
Hansen, Arthur G. (C)
Harder, Edwin L.
Harris, Milton
Haus, Hermann A.
Hauspurg, Arthur

Heinemann, Heinz
Hendrie, Joseph M.
Hertzberg, Abraham
Hess, Wilmot N.
Hittinger, William C.
Holley, Charles H.
Johnson, Joe W.
Johnson, Robert L.
Jordan, Donald J.
Keenan, Joseph H.†
Keyes, Robert W.
Kilgore, Lee A.
Kino, Gordon S.
Lamm, A. Uno†
Lapidus, Leon†
Levenson, Milton
Ling, Joseph T.
Linsley, Ray K.
Longwell, John P.
Lundin, Bruce T.
Mackenzie, John D.
Marcatili, Enrique A. J.
Mark, Hans
Metzger, Sidney
Misch, Herbert L.
Mitchell, James K.
Moore, Gordon E.
Moreell, Ben†
Morse, Richard S.†
Mumma, Albert G.
Murray, Peter
O'Neill, Eugene F.
Ongerth, Henry J.
Parker, Jack S.
Parker, Norman F.
Pigford, Thomas H.
Popov, Egor P.
Rabinow, Jacob
Reissner, Eric
Reswick, James B.
Russell, Allen S. (C)
Schechter, Robert S.
Schuhmann, Reinhardt, Jr.
Slepian, David
Slichter, William P.
Stern, Arthur C.
Straiton, Archie W.
Sze, Morgan C.
Thomas, Harold A., Jr.
Tien, Chang-Lin
Van Dyke, Milton D.
von Gierke, Henning E.
Wachtman, John B., Jr.
Webster, William M.
Weertman, Johannes

Weston, Roy F.
Whitcomb, Richard T.
Wilkins, J. Ernest, Jr.
Yariv, Amnon
Yee, Alfred A.

1977

Acrivos, Andreas
Alfrey, Turner, Jr.†
Anderson, Arthur R.
Apstein, Maurice†
Arbiter, Nathaniel
Backus, John
Baron, Thomas†
Beaton, Roy H.
Bell, C. Gordon
Bellman, Richard E.†
Berlekamp, Elwyn R.
Bogdonoff, Seymour M.
Bridges, William B.
Copeland, Norman A.†
Crandall, Stephen H.
D'Appolonia, Elio
Dean, Robert C., Jr.
Degenkolb, Henry J.
Desoer, Charles A.
Dukler, A. E.
Eberhart, Howard D.
Eisenbud, Merril
Felsen, Leopold B.
Gautreaux, Marcelian F.
Geer, Ronald L.
Glaser, Edward L.
Hall, Robert N.
Hansen, Grant L.
Harris, Stephen E.
Harris, William J., Jr.
Harwood, Julius J.
Hellwarth, Robert W.
Hodge, Philip G., Jr.
Hogan, C. Lester
Holmes, D. Brainerd
Irwin, George R.
Isaacs, John D.†
Jennings, Burgess H.
Jennings, Paul C.
Kane, Eneas D.
Kantrowitz, Arthur
Kays, William M.
Kesler, Clyde E.
Kuesel, Thomas R.
Lambertsen, Christian J.
Laufer, John†
Ling, Frederick F.

Loofbourrow, Alan G.
Luerssen, Frank W.
Lundstrom, Louis C.
Mager, Artur
McCabe, Warren L.†
McCarty, Perry L.
McKinney, Ross E.
Mills, G. Alexander
Morgan, Paul W.
Olsen, Kenneth H.
Owen, Walter S.
Penner, Stanford S.
Penzien, Joseph
Perlis, Alan J.
Poundstone, William N.
Prater, C. Dwight
Probstein, Ronald F.
Rasmussen, Norman C.
Rice, Stephen O.†
Roberts, Richard W.†
Rowe, Joseph E.
Sammet, Jean E.
Saville, Thorndike, Jr.
Schade, Otto H., Sr.†
Scisson, Sidney E.
Sozen, Mete A.
Squires, Arthur M.
Starr, Eugene C.†
Steinberg, Morris A.
Stookey, Stanley D.
Swabb, Lawrence E., Jr.
Swearingen, Judson S.
Trump, John G.†
Vanoni, Vito A.
Vogel, Herbert D.†
Vollum, C. Howard†
von Hippel, Arthur R.
Wait, James R.
Weisz, Paul B.
Wertheim, Robert H.
Widmer, Robert H.
Woll, Edward
Woodward, Richard L.†
Wooldridge, Dean E.
Yardley, John F.

1978

Albaugh, Fred W.
Alexander, William D.
Allen, Lew, Jr. (C)
Armstrong, Neil A.
Avery, Robert
Bandel, Hannskarl
Baron, Melvin L.

Bleich, Hans H.†
Bolt, Bruce A.
Bolt, Richard H.
Boulger, Francis W.
Bovay, Harry E., Jr.
Boyer, Raymond F.
Brown, David
Burks, G. Edwin
Cluff, Lloyd S.
Coble, Robert L.
Concordia, Charles
Corry, Andrew F.
Cragon, Harvey G.
Crane, L. Stanley
Deschamps, Georges A.
Dickeman, Raymond L.†
Elder, Rex A.
Eshleman, Von R.
Etherington, Harold
Evans, David C.
Everhart, Thomas E. (C)
Flanagan, James L.
Frazier, J. Earl†
Garwin, Richard L.
Gilkeson, Robert F.
Gross, Eric T. B.†
Hamilton, William T.
Hatsopoulos, George N. (C)
Herman, Robert
Hicks, Beatrice†
Hogg, David C.
Hosler, Charles L., Jr.
Hudson, Herbert E., Jr.†
Jeffs, George W.
Kellogg, Herbert H.
Kerrebrock, Jack L.
Kouts, Herbert J. C.
Landauer, Rolf
Lang, William W.
Larson, Thurston E.†
Leathers, J. F. M.†
Lee, William S.
LeMessurier, William J.
Lischer, Ludwig F.
Low, John R., Jr.
Lucas, William R.
Lucky, Robert W.
MacPherson, Herbert G.
Marcuvitz, Nathan
May, Walter G.
Meindl, James D.
Meyerand, Russell G., Jr.
Mickley, Harold S.
Moeller, Dade W.
Moore, John R.

Moore, William W.
Morgan, James J.
Morrow, Walter E., Jr.
Mueser, William H.†
O'Connor, Donald J.
Oppenheim, Antoni K.
Ostrach, Simon
Parker, Herbert M.†
Patel, C. Kumar N.
Paxton, Harold W.
Peterson, Harold A.
Plummer, James W.
Poettmann, Fred H.
Promisel, Nathan E.
Quinn, John A.
Roberts, George A.
Roberts, Lawrence G.
Roe, Kenneth A.
Roshko, Anatol
Rudd, Dale F.
Saffer, Alfred
Schmitt, Roland W. (C)
Scordelis, Alexander C.
Scriven, L. E.
Seban, Ralph A.
Shinozuka, Masanobu
Skromme, Lawrence H.
Staehle, Roger W.
Steiner, John E.
Stewart, Robert E.†
Swenson, George W., Jr.
Swerling, Peter
Thurlimann, Bruno
van der Ziel, Aldert
Viest, Ivan M.
Viterbi, Andrew J.
Wei, James
Whitby, Kenneth T.†

1979

Aaron, M. Robert
Allen, Herbert
Anderson, John G.
Austin, T. Louis, Jr.
Baker, James G.
Berger, Bernard B.
Berkey, Donald C.
Blecher, Franklin H.
Bloor, W. Spencer
Boileau, Oliver C.
Boudart, Michel
Bray, A. Philip
Bresler, Boris
Cocke, John

Cooke, J. Barry
Crocco, Luigi†
Donaldson, Coleman duPont
Drickamer, Harry G.
Duwez, Pol E.†
Elias, Peter
Everett, Robert R.
Feely, Frank J., Jr.
Finnie, Iain
Fischer, Irene K.
Freudenstein, Ferdinand
Fung, Yuan-Cheng B.
Gagge, A. Pharo
Galambos, Theodore V.
Gallager, Robert G.
Galloway, William J.
Gasich, Welko E.
Gee, Edwin A.
Gordon, Eugene I.
Goss, Floyd L.†
Grove, Andrew S.
Halbouty, Michel T.
Hathaway, Gail A.†
Heilmeier, George H.
Hoag, David G.
Holtby, Kenneth F.
Hooven, Frederick J.†
Horton, Billy M.
Howard, William J.
Iverson, Kenneth E.
Jaicks, Frederick G.
Jarrett, Noel
Johnston, Bruce G.
Kane, Edward R. (T)
Kear, Bernard H.
Keulegan, Garbis H.
Kimbark, Edward W.†
Kirchmayer, Leon K.
Law, Harold B.†
Lightfoot, Edwin N., Jr.
Linvill, William K.†
London, A. L.
MacCready, Paul B.
Mathews, Max V.
Maurer, Robert D.
Mayo, John S.
McClelland, Bramlette
McCune, William J., Jr.
Metzner, Arthur B.
Michaels, Alan S.
Morris, John W.
Murden, William R., Jr.
Neal, Richard B.
Northrop, John K.†
Peltier, Eugene J.

Plesset, Milton S.
Prausnitz, John M.
Rannie, W. Duncan†
Reed, Irving S.
Reynolds, William C.
Robinson, Thomas B.
Schmitt, Otto H.
Schroeder, Manfred R.
Sechler, Ernest E.†
Sherby, Oleg D.
Shewmon, Paul G.
Singleton, Henry E.
Snitzer, Elias
Snyder, J. Edward, Jr.
Squire, Alexander
Staszesky, Francis M.
Stern, Theodore
Summerfield, Martin
Taylor, Charles E.
Tellep, Daniel M.
Tulin, Marshall P.
Veletsos, Anestis S.
Wadsworth, Milton E.
Weber, Eugene W.†
Weeks, Wilford F.
Welch, Lloyd R.
Wentorf, Robert H., Jr.
Wernick, Jack H.
West, John M.

1980

Adamson, Arthur P.
Amirikian, Arsham
Atwood, Donald J. (C)
Barkan, Philip
Baron, Seymour
Batchelor, John W.
Behnke, Wallace B.
Bloch, Erich
Boyer, Vincent S.
Brannon, H. Raymond, Jr.
Brenner, Howard
Cleveland, Frank A.†
Conwell, Esther M.
Corcoran, William H.†
Corrsin, Stanley†
Covert, Eugene E.
Crain, Cullen M.
Crombie, Douglass D.
Cruz, Jose B., Jr.
Dean, Robert G.
Decker, Raymond F.
Dirks, Leslie C.
Dolan, John E.

Duffy, Robert A.
Elkins, Lincoln F.
Frank, Richard S.†
Garbarini, Edgar J.
Geist, Jacob M.
Grant, Nicholas J.
Hamming, Richard W.
Hartley, Fred L.
Hemsworth, Martin C.
Hoffman, John D.
Hood, Edward E., Jr.
Hulm, John K.
Ingard, K. Uno
Isakoff, Sheldon E.
Iselin, Donald G.
Johnson, I. Birger
Kalb, John W.
Kimmons, George H.
Kleinrock, Leonard
Kobayashi, Shiro
Kressel, Henry
Kuhrt, Wesley A.†
Landweber, Louis
Lang, Martin
Laudise, Robert A.
Lee, Griff C.
Li, Tingye
McMahon, Charles J., Jr.
Mergler, Harry W.
Monismith, Carl L.
Newell, Allen
Norris, Karl H.
Oder, Frederic C. E.
Oldshue, James Y.
Pister, Karl S.
Reid, Robert C.
Rice, James R.
Richardson, Herbert H. (C)
Robeck, Gordon G.
Rumsey, Victor H.
Schaefer, Jacob W.
Schubauer, Galen B.
Schurman, Glenn A.
Sternlicht, Beno
Swiger, William F.
Thiele, Ernest W.
Thompson, Ken
Throdahl, Monte C.
Vanderslice, Thomas A.
Vassell, Gregory S.
von Ohain, Hans J. P.
Wehausen, John V.
Welch, Jasper A., Jr.
Westwood, Albert R. C.
Wilson, Gerald L.

Withington, Holden W.
Wolfe, Bertram
Yih, Chia-Shun
Young, Laurence R.

1981

Barthold, Lionel O.
Beck, Paul A.
Breakwell, John V.
Buckley, Page S.
Chao, Bei Tse
Codd, Edgar F.
Compton, W. Dale
Cook, Thomas B., Jr.
Core, Jesse F.
Cornell, C. Allin
Corson, Dale R.
Creagan, Robert J.
Crooke, Robert C.
Dakin, Thomas W.
DeBra, Daniel B.
Duncan, Robert C.
Estcourt, Vivian F.†
Fisher, John C.
Graff, George S.
Green, Paul E., Jr.
Gyftopoulos, Elias P.
Hammond, David G.
Happel, John
Harrington, Dean B.
Harter, George A.
Harvey, Douglass C.
Herrmann, George
Joel, Amos E., Jr.
Johnson, Reynold B.
Johnston, Roy G.
King, C. Judson
Klebanoff, Philip S.
Kline, Stephen J.
Knuth, Donald E.
Koch, Leonard J.
Kohler, Max A.
Lafferty, James M.
Landis, John W.
Mar, James W.
McCarthy, John F., Jr.†
Meisel, Seymour L.
Noble, Charles C.
O'Brien, Brian
Pings, Cornelius J.
Queneau, Paul E.
Ramey, Henry J., Jr.
Rich, Ben R.
Rocheleau, Robert F.

Sandberg, Irwin W.
Sarkaria, Gurmukh S.
Savage, Warren F.†
Schey, John A.
Schroepfer, George J.†
Spoelhof, Charles P.
Stekly, Z. J. John
Stibitz, George R.
Stone, Henry E.
Stratton, James Hobson†
Syvertson, Clarence A.
Van Uitert, Le Grand
VerSnyder, Francis L.
Weimer, Paul K.
Zebroski, Edwin L.

1982

Achenbach, Jan D.
Agbabian, Mihran S.
Chin, Gilbert Y.
Dietz, William C.
Dunn, Floyd
Eagleson, Peter S.
Flipse, John E.
Garry, Frederick W.
Gerber, H. Joseph
Gold, Bernard
Hansen, Kent F.
Haughton, Kenneth E.
Henle, Robert A.†
Heppe, R. Richard
Herriott, Donald R.
Jacobs, Irwin M.
Jones, Trevor O.
Kestin, Joseph
Ketchum, Milo S.
Krebs, James N.
Kunzler, John E.
Leith, Emmett N.
Leitmann, George
Leonhard, William E.
Matlock, Hudson
McHenry, Keith W., Jr.
Melcher, James R.
Moorhouse, Douglas C.
Opie, William R.
Oshman, M. Kenneth
Robb, Walter L.
Rolfe, Stanley T.
Roth, James F.
Russell, Donald G.
Schowalter, William R.
Schwan, Judith A.
Scott, John W.

Searle, Willard F., Jr.
Seinfeld, John H.
Slaughter, John B.
Szebehely, Victor
Szekely, Julian
Thomas, Gareth
Vine, Allyn C.
Wang, An
Weidlinger, Paul
Winsche, Warren E.†
Wu, Theodore Y.
Youla, Dante C.

1983

Augustine, Norman R.
Baum, Richard T.
Bement, Arden L., Jr.
Bollinger, John G.
Cleasby, John L.
Coover, Harry W.
Cross, L. Eric
Deming, W. Edwards
Drew, Thomas B.†
Eckert, Charles A.
Forney, G. David, Jr.
Gallagher, Richard H.
Gatos, Harry C.
Gens, Ralph S.
Gratch, Serge
Hall, Wilfred M.†
Hendron, Alfred J., Jr.
Hodge, Raymond J.
Hodges, David A.
Hough, Richard R.
Hutchinson, John W.
Jasny, George R.
Ladd, Charles C.
Laning, J. Halcombe
Loehr, Raymond C.
Logue, Joseph C.
McWhorter, Alan L.
Monson, Harry O.
Muskat, Morris
Nadel, Norman A.
Nierenberg, William A.
Palmer, Ralph L.
Pritchard, Dalton H.
Rabiner, Lawrence R.
Rowe, Brian H.
Salvadori, Mario G.
Schurmeier, Harris M.
Shank, Charles V.
Shank, Maurice E.
Smith, George E.

Smith, Kenneth A.
Sterzer, Fred
Stevens, William D.
Stuart, Derald A.
Themelis, Nickolas J.
Tobias, Charles W.
Welch, John F., Jr. (Ch)
White, Willis S., Jr.
Zia, Paul

1984

Aldrich, Harl P., Jr.
Allen, Dell K.
Anders, William A.
Ashkin, Arthur
Bloembergen, Nicolaas
Burtis, Theodore A.
Chopra, Anil K.
Coar, Richard J.
Coles, Donald E.
Dally, James W.
de Mello, F. Paul
Dennard, Robert H.
Engelberger, Joseph F.
Evans, John V.
Feiner, Alexander
Fox, Daniel W.†
Hahn, Robert S.
Hanson, Robert D.
Holzman, Albert G.†
Jenkins, Lawrence E.
Kahles, John F.
Kailath, Thomas
Kaminow, Ivan P.
Kuehler, Jack D.
Lampson, Butler W.
Leonard, John W.
Lett, Philip W.
Leverett, Miles C.
Likins, Peter W.
Luss, Dan
Mayer, James W.
McCall, David W.
McCarthy, Walter J., Jr.
Mead, Carver A.
Mehrabian, Robert
Moore, Franklin K.
Murrin, Thomas J.
Naghdi, Paul M.
Napadensky, Hyla S.
Perkins, Thomas K.
Reddy, D. Raj
Reshotko, Eli
Sanchini, Dominick J.

Schmertmann, John H.
Schmitz, Roger A.
Smith, Joseph L., Jr.
Sowman, Harold G.
Splinter, William E.
Standing, Marshall B.
Sutherland, G. Russell
Sutter, Joseph F.
Thomas, Leo J.
Tiemann, Jerome J.
Tiffany, Charles F.
Walker, Leland J.
Weinig, Sheldon
Wilson, Basil W.
Zaborszky, John

1985

Adams, Richard E.
Bowers, Klaus D.
Burstein, Sol
Calhoun, John C., Jr.
Cho, Alfred Y.
Christiansen, John V.
Condit, Philip M.
Cook, Paul M.
Cooper, William E.
Dantzig, George B.
Duncan, James M.
Emmert, Richard E.
Fowler, Charles A.
Fraser, Donald C.
Fridley, Robert B.
Geddes, Leslie A.
Goldstein, Richard J.
Gordon, James P.
Gummel, Hermann K.
Hawkins, Robert C.
Henry, Allan F.
Hodges, Lawrence H.
Howard, William G., Jr.
Ippen, Erich P.
Kehrl, Howard H.
Lardner, James F.
Larson, Thomas D. (C)
Latanision, Ronald M.
Lee, Shih-Ying
Luborsky, Fred E.
Lyons, John W.
MacChesney, John B.
Marks, Craig
Matthews, Charles S.
McDonnell, Sanford N.
Messinger, Richard C.
Morse, Philip M.†

Owen, Warren H.
Pao, Yih-Hsing
Peterson, George P.
Price, Robert
Pritsker, A. Alan B.
Reid, Robert O.
Rhodes, Allen F.
Rivlin, Ronald S.
Rosensweig, Ronald E.
Schmit, Lucien A., Jr.
Seebass, A. Richard
Sevin, Eugene
Shannon, Claude E.
Shen, Shan-Fu
Shinnar, Reuel
Snyder, Franklin F.
Somasundaran, Ponisseril
Spiess, Fred Noel
Sprague, Robert C.
Stephens, Charles W.
Stillman, Gregory E.
Sumner, Eric E.
Traub, Joseph F.
Turin, George L.
Ware, Willis H.
Weber, Walter J., Jr.
Weekman, Vern W., Jr.
Widnall, Sheila E.
Wilson, Edward L.
Yachnis, Michael

1986

Allen, William F., Jr.
Atlas, David
Bailey, James E.
Billington, David P.
Bowen, H. Kent
Brown, Walter L.
Cashen, John F.
Clagett, Robert P.
Conway, Richard A.
Curtin, Robert H.
Denn, Morton M.
Eastman, Lester F.
Feigenbaum, Edward A.
Fisher, John W.
Focht, John A., Jr.
Galt, John K.
Holm, L. W.
Iacocca, Lee A.
Idol, James D., Jr.
Iorillo, Anthony J.
Jansen, Robert B.
Jefferson, Edward G.

Jones, Thomas V.
Jordan, Angel G.
Kobayashi, Albert S.
Kummer, Joseph T.
Lathrop, Kaye D.
Lo, Yuen Tze
Lubinski, Arthur
Mei, Chiang C.
Mirels, Harold
Moore, Joseph B.
Morrow, Richard M.
Moses, Joel
Mura, Toshio
Nadler, Gerald
Nemhauser, George L.
Nielsen, Jack N.
Oldham, William G.
Panish, Morton B.
Pankove, Jacques I.
Park, Robert H.
Paulling, J. Randolph
Pfender, Emil
Plonsey, Robert
Poduska, John W.
Prats, Michael
Pulling, Ronald W.
Redington, Rowland W.
Rivard, Jerome G.
Sah, Chih-Tang
Sakshaug, Eugene C.
Samara, George A.
Scott, Charles D.
Shaw, Herbert John
Silcox, William H.
Skolnik, Merrill I.
Smerdon, Ernest T.
Sparrow, Ephraim M.
Stein, Dale F.
Stevens, Kenneth N.
Tang, Chung L.
Tape, Gerald F.
Torgersen, Paul E.
Troiano, Alexander R.
Veinott, Arthur F., Jr.
Wang, Daniel I. C.
Weiss, Max T.
Wheeler, Harold A.
Whitney, Eugene C.
Williams, Sam B.
Wise, John J.
Yates, Alden P.†

1987

Allen, Frances E.

Armstrong, John A.
Atal, Bishnu S.
Bell, Alexis T.
Blenkarn, Kenneth A.
Bose, Amar G.
Brill, Yvonne C.
Broadwell, James E.
Brown, Kermit E.
Bugliarello, George (C)
Byer, Robert L.
Byrd, Lloyd G.
Carroll, Michael M.
Carroll, William J.
Carstensen, Edwin L.
Cheng, Herbert S.
Chittenden, William A.
Christensen, Richard M.
Chu, Richard C.
Conn, Robert W.
Cutler, Leonard S.
Duderstadt, James J.
Duscha, Lloyd A.
Economy, James
Ellert, Frederick J.
Elverum, Gerard W., Jr.
Giacco, Alexander F.
Glass, Alastair M.
Good, Mary L. (C)
Goodman, Joseph W.
Gossard, Arthur C.
Grant, Eugene L.
Hammond, Donald L.
Heller, Adam
Hiler, Edward A.
Ho, Yu-Chi
Johnson, Herbert H.
Kahn, Robert E.
Kanninen, Melvin F.
Keller, Jack
LaBerge, Walter B.
LaMoreaux, Philip E., Sr.
Laubach, Gerald D.
Leal, L. Gary
Lepselter, Martin P.
Li, Yao Tzu
Lieberman, Gerald J.
Liu, Benjamin Y. H.
Lomax, Harvard
Maslen, Stephen H.
McCarthy, John
McNown, John S.
Miller, William F.
Morkovin, Mark V.
Narath, Albert
Nix, William D.

Odeh, Aziz S.
Oppenheim, Alan V.
Ormsby, Robert B., Jr.
Papay, Lawrence T.
Pipes, R. Byron
Riggs, Louis W.
Roy, Della M.
Scanlan, Robert H.
Stalkup, Fred I.
Sternling, Charles V.
Strecker, William D.
Streetman, Ben G.
Tai, Chen-To
Tapley, Byron D.
Tucker, Richard F.
Vallerga, Bernard A.
Vincenti, Walter G.
Viskanta, Raymond
Waggoner, Eugene B.
Welliver, Albertus D.
Westerberg, Arthur W.
White, John A., Jr.
Wilczynski, Janusz S.
Williams, James C.
Wong, Eugene
Zarem, Abe M.

1988

Adams, Laurence J.
Alkire, Richard C.
Andrews, Frederick T., Jr.
Ballhaus, William F., Jr.
Berg, Robert R.
Birnbaum, Howard K.
Bischoff, Kenneth B.
Brodersen, Robert W.
Caudle, Ben H.
Chang, Leroy L.
Chaudhari, Praveen
Cheng, Hsien K.
Claerbout, Jon F.

Coats, Keith H.
Cohen, Aaron
Cook, Neville G.W.
Cording, Edward J.
Coulter, James B.
Curry, Norval H.
Curtis, Lawrence B.
Daman, Ernest L.
Davis, H. Ted
Eastman, Dean E.
Edwards, Helen T.
Elliott, Robert S.
Fox, George A.
Googin, John M.
Gould, James P.
Greatbatch, Wilson
Hecker, Siegfried S.
Hingorani, Narain G.
Hsu, Chieh-Su
Jensen, Marvin E.
Jirsa, James O.
Johnson, Ellis L.
Judge, Frank D.
Junkins, Jerry R.
Juran, Joseph M.
Keller, George E., II
Koff, Bernard L.
Krogh, Lester C.
Lanzerotti, Louis J.
Lemke, James U.
Leonards, Gerald A.
Liskov, Barbara H.
Macovski, Albert
Maneatis, George A.
Mason, John L.
May, Bill B.
McRuer, Duane T.
Mead, Lawrence M., Jr.
Mitter, Sanjoy K.
Mize, Joe H.
Mooney, John B., Jr.
Mote, Clayton D., Jr.

Nerem, Robert M.
Norris, William C.
Oden, J. Tinsley
Otte, Carel
Parker, Frank L.
Parker, Ronald R.
Paul, Donald R.
Peline, Val P.
Petersen, Donald E.
Pian, Theodore H.H.
Pomerene, James H.
Procknow, Donald E.
Rapp, Robert A.
Richardson, Joseph G.
Ritchie, Dennis M.
Robinson, Enders A.
Shaw, Don W.
Silverman, Leonard M.
Simpson, Joanne
Simpson, John A.
Skalak, Richard
Smith, Leroy H., Jr.
Spencer, William J.
Tarjan, Robert E.
Thompson, David A.
Todreas, Neil E.
Weertman, Julia R.
Welber, Irwin
Williams, Forman A.
Winer, Ward O.

1989

Amann, Charles
Annestrand, Stig A.
Aplan, Frank F.
Archer, David H.
Argon, Ali S.
Auston, David H.
Bea, Robert G.
Bekey, George A.
Betti, John A.

Beyster, J. Robert
Birnbaum, Joel S.
Boothroyd, Geoffrey
Carberry, James J.
Caren, Robert P.
Casani, John R.
Clifton, Rodney J.
Conway, Lynn A.
Damon, Richard W.
Director, Stephen W.
Doyle, Frederick J.
Dunford, Edsel D.
Dupuis, Russell D.
Eaton, Robert J.
Elachi, Charles
Falkie, Thomas V.
Fang, Frank F.
Fischell, Robert E.
Forney, Robert C.
Forsen, Harold K.
Garmire, Elsa M.
Geselowitz, David B.
Gilbert, Jerome B.
Goldman, Alan J.
Goldsmith, Werner
Gruy, Henry J.
Gubbins, Keith E.
Hall, Carl W.
Hartmanis, Juris
Hatzakis, Michael
Hearth, Donald P.
Hegedus, L. Louis
Hermann, Robert J.
Hill, George R.
Hoel, Lester A.
Hopcroft, John E.
Idriss, Izzat M.
Joklik, Gunther F.
Kolff, Willem J.
Kramer, Edward J.
Little, John D. C.
Loucks, Daniel P.

Mast, Robert F.
Matsuoka, Shiro
McBee, Frank W., Jr.
McDonald, John C.
Minsky, Marvin L.
Mitchell, James W.
Moore, Richard K.
Netravali, Arun N.
Newman, J. Nicholas
Newnham, Robert E.
Nordgren, Ronald P.
Oglesby, Clarkson H.
O'Melia, Charles R.
Rediker, Robert H.
Rohrer, Ronald A.
Rutan, Elbert L.
Scherer, Harold N., Jr.
Schriesheim, Alan
Schuh, Frank J.
Seifert, Laurence C.
Shuler, Michael L.
Smith, A.M.O.
Smith, Henry I.
Solberg, James J.
Strauch, Richard G.
Tasch, Al F., Jr.
Thompson, Larry F.
Thompson, Philip A.
Till, Charles E.
Ullman, Jeffrey D.
van Schilfgaarde, Jan
Wang, Kuo K.
Ward, William J., III
White, J. Edward
White, Robert M.
Witherspoon, Paul A., Jr.
Woodall, Jerry M.
Wygnanski, Israel J.
Yu, A. Tobey

Foreign Associates

by year of election

1976

Ackeret, Jakob†
Aigrain, Pierre R.
Angelini, Arnaldo M.
Brard, Roger E.M.†
Casimir, H. B. G.
Cottrell, Alan
Crussard, Charles
Dassault, Marcel†
Davidson, J. F.
Finsterwalder, Ulrich†
Hall, Arnold
Hawthorne, William R.
Hill, John
Hinton, Christopher†
Ibuka, Masaru
Kenedi, Robert M.
Lewis, W. Bennett†
Mandel, Heinrich†
Richardson, F. Denys†
Skempton, Alec W.

1977

Ailleret, Pierre M.
Bowen, Edward G.
Chesters, John H.
Esaki, Leo
Giraud, Andre
Hafele, Wolf
Inouye, Goro†
Jancke, Gunnar

Kaczmarek, Jan
Kobayashi, Koji
Koiter, Warner T.
Kurdjumov, Georgy V.
Lighthill, M. James
Moe, Johannes
Ospina, Carlos S.
Peters, Jacques
Rosenblueth, Emilio
Rumpf, Hans†
Rusch, Hubert†
Wilkes, Maurice V.

1978

Abrahamsen, Egil
Ando, Yoshio
Danckwerts, Peter V.†
Davies, Duncan S.†
Dhawan, Satish
Gunn, John B.
Ipponmatsu, Tamaki†
Kogelnik, Herwig
Kramers, Hendrik
Massonnet, Charles E.
McLennan, Ian
Muto, Kiyoshi
Neporozhny, Pyotr S.
Pelegrin, Marc J.
Schulten, Rudolf
Scovil, H. E. D.
Smith, Harold A.
Vendryes, Georges Andre
   Charles
Zeevaert, Leonardo

1979

Barlow, Harold E. M.†
Bruel, Per V.

Eklund, Sigvard
Forrest, John S.
Fuwa, Tasuku
Germain, Paul
Govier, George W.
Hug, Michel
Krishna, Jai
Magnien, Maurice
Marshall, Walter Charles
Oatley, Charles
Paton, Angus
Saunders, Owen
Silver, Robert S.
Tani, Itiro
Whittle, Frank
Yoshida, Fumitake

1980

de Mello, Victor F. B.
Farmer, Frank Reginald
Frank, Charles
Kilburn, Tom
Malavard, Lucien C.
Mason, Stanley G.†
Pearson, John R. A.
Rowe, Roy E.

1981

Denbigh, Kenneth G.
Haasen, Peter
Hooker, Stanley George†
Lyse, Inge Martin
Pestel, Eduard C.
Rivas-Mijares, Gustavo
Singer, Josef
Spur, Gunter
Yagi, Sakae
Yokobori, Takeo

Zienkiewicz, Olgierd C.
Zuse, Konrad

1982

Fant, Gunnar
Ingerslev, Fritz
Levich, Benjamin G.†
Mao, Yi-Sheng T. E.
Nishiyama, Zenji
Oswatitsch, Klaus

1983

Gabrielli, Giuseppe†
Hilsum, Cyril
Leonhardt, Fritz
Nicholson, Robin B.
Wicke, Ewald

1984

Barrere, Marcel L. J.
Galloway, Donald F.
Seippel, Claude P.†
Shchukin, Eugene D.
Topsoe, Haldor F. A.

1985

Hatvany, Jozsef†
Inose, Hiroshi
LaQue, Francis L.†
Malpas, Robert
Uenohara, Michiyuki

1986

Argyris, John
Chisholm, Donald A.

Clarke, Arthur C.
Habibie, Bacharuddin J.
Kelly, Anthony
Mori, Yasuo

1987

Davenport, Alan G.
Downs, Diarmuid
Embleton, Tony F. W.
Gauvin, William H.
Hayashi, Tsuyoshi
Kikuchi, Makoto
Rooke, Denis

1988

Dietz, Daniel N.†
Horlock, John H.
Lange, Kurt H.
Legget, Robert F.
Matoba, Sachio†
Rodriguez-Iturbe, Ignacio
Ziv, Jacob

1989

Ager-Hanssen, Henrik
Colombo, Umberto P.
Frolov, Konstantin V.
List, Hans
Narasimha, Roddam
Vasco Costa, Fernando
Zakai, Moshe

APPENDIX B

NAE Staff Members

The following list reflects members of the NAE staff who have served for a minimum of one year; the position titles listed are the last position held. Although every effort was made to develop a complete list, early personnel records were not comprehensive, so some information may be incorrectly shown or omitted.

Anderson, Caroline, administrative secretary, Program Office, 1986–1988

Andresen, Jeanne, assistant director, Membership Office, 1989–present

Armstrong, Saundra, administrative assistant, Membership Office, 1989–present

Atkinson, Pamela, NAE Fellow, 1987–1988

Ausubel, Jesse, director, Program Office, 1982–1988

Ball, Mary "Jay", administrative assistant, Program Office, 1986–present

Beaudin, Marlene (Phillips), director, Office of Administration, Finance, and Public Awareness, 1983–present

Becker, Barbara, administrative assistant, Office of the Foreign Secretary, 1987–present

Berry, Nancy, senior secretary, Office of Administration, Finance, and Public Awareness, 1988–present

Bishop, Barbara, administrative assistant, Office of Administration, Finance, and Public Awareness, 1980–present

Brandt, Deborah, director, Membership Office, 1984–present

Burger, Robert, executive director, 1967–1979

Carson, Claudia, secretary, 1970–1971

Chin, Vivienne, administrative assistant, Program Office, 1989–present

Collins, Elsie, secretary, 1971–1972

Compton, W. Dale, NAE Senior Fellow, 1986–1988

Crowell, Sharon, administrative secretary, Office of Administration, Finance, and Public Awareness, 1989–present

Cunningham, Ersell, administrative assistant, Membership Office, 1985–1988

Davis, Mary (Wade), administrative assistant, 1973–1979

Doody, Judith (Hanzook), associate for financial administration, Office of Administration, Finance, and Public Awareness, 1985–present

Dorais, Deborah (Jolly), administrative secretary, Development Office, 1985–1987

Echohawk, Bernadette, administrative assistant, Membership Office, 1986–1987

Ekelman, Karen, NAE Fellow, 1985–1987

Embree, Joan, secretary, 1966–1967

Fisher, Theresa, secretary, 1968–1970

Garcia, Kimberly (Hummer), administrative assistant, Office of Administration, Finance, and Public Awareness, 1984–present

Gemmell, Lynn, editor, 1967–1970

Gibbs, Penelope, administrative supervisor, Program Office, 1984–1988

Gipson, Melvin, associate for public awareness, Program Office, 1987–present

Grim, Ruth, secretary, 1971–1973

Guile, Bruce, director, Program Office, 1984–present

Hale, Billie, assistant for membership services, 1980–1984

Hamilton, Glenda, secretary, 1980–1982

Harris, Ann, personal secretary, 1970–1972

Harrison, Donna, administrative coordinator, Office of the President, 1984–1985

Harrison, Virginia, executive assistant for membership, 1981–1984

Helm, John, NAE Fellow, 1987–1989

Hightower, Frances, assistant for planning and administration, 1970–1972

Holladay, Christine, secretary, 1965–1967

Holland, Carol, senior secretary, Membership Office, 1986–1987

Howard, William, NAE Senior Fellow, 1987–present

Hubbard, Denise, administrative assistant, Development Office, 1988–present

Huff, Barbara (Neff), executive associate, Office of the President, 1983–present

Huntley, Delores, membership assistant,

Membership Office, 1986–present

Jacob, Jeanne, director, Development Office, 1984–present

Janson, Bette, administrative assistant, Office of the Home Secretary, 1988–present

Jones, Mary, secretary, 1970–1978

Jones, Marybeth, administrative assistant, 1980–1982

Kaffee, Naomi, administrative assistant, 1976–1978

Kaplan, Ruth, executive assistant for administration, 1973–1984

Keith, Karen, administrative assistant, Membership Office, 1987–1988

Keitz, Maribeth, program assistant, Program Office, 1989–present

King, Randolph, executive officer, 1979–1982

Koustenis, Christina, administrative secretary, Membership Office, 1983–1984

Langford, H. Dale, editor, 1985–present

Levandoski, Carrie, associate director and public awareness officer, Office of Administration, Finance, and Public Awareness, 1983–present

Little, Catharine, program assistant, 1973–1974

Martinez, Lissa, NAE Fellow, 1984–1985

McDermott, Nancy, executive assistant, Office of the President, 1984–1988

McNeil, Annette, senior secretary, Program Office, 1987–1989

Michael, Betty, secretary, 1979–1980

Miller, Hugh, executive officer, 1971–1986

Money, Anne, administrative assistant, Office of the President, 1988–present

Moore, Gale (Munson), secretary, 1976–1978

Mulligan, James, Jr., executive officer, 1968–1974

Mullins, Roberta, secretary, 1968–1969

Muroyama, Janet, program associate, Program Office, 1985–1988

Nelson, E. Henriette, executive assistant for membership, 1967–1980

Olsen, Eileen, secretary, 1968–1970

Parlor, Angela, administrative secretary, Development Office, 1989–present

Parrington, Jean, administrative assistant, 1965–1970

Phibbs, Nancy, administrative assistant, Membership Office, 1984–1986

Pollack, Kerstin (Binns), assistant to the secretary, 1965–1983

Pomeroy, Marjorie, administrative assistant, Program Office, 1984–1988

Powers, Mary, research assistant, Development Office, 1987–1988

Prue, Penny, secretary, 1969–1974

Radany, Ernest, assistant to the executive officer, 1972–1978

Reid, Proctor, NAE Fellow, 1988–present

Renshof, Barbara, financial assistant, Office of Administration, Finance, and Public Awareness, 1988–present

Rishoi, Thomas, management assistant, 1969–1970

Rivard, Michele, NAE Intern, 1988–1989

Rivers, Wanda, administrative assistant, Development Office, 1988–1989

Robinson, Norma, fiscal assistant, 1971–1973

Rod, Samuel, associate director, Program Office, 1989–present

Rodriguez, Lady, administrative secretary, Office of External Affairs, 1980–1987

Salmon, William, executive officer, 1986–present

Scales, Patricia, senior secretary, Membership Office, 1987–present

Shumaker, Dorothy, secretary to the president, 1969–1983

Sims, Benta, executive assistant, Office of the President, 1986–1988

Skapars, Linda, administrative assistant, Membership Office, 1986–1987

Skomal, Susan, research assistant, Development Office, 1984–1986

Sladovich, Hedy, research assistant/assistant editor, Program Office, 1988–present

Smith, Belinda, executive assistant, Executive Office, 1972–present

Sowers, Marty, office assistant, 1972–1973

Spencer, Susanna, research assistant, Development Office, 1987–present

Stern, Robert, executive secretary, 1967–1970

von Meister, Leila, executive assistant, 1970–1978

Walton, M. Frances, administrative assistant, Office of the Foreign Secretary, 1983–1984

Watson, Eunice, administrative assistant, 1971–1974

Weatherby, Dorothy, communications assistant, 1968–1970

Wolf, Julia, development associate, Development Office, 1985–present

Wolford, Douglas, public awareness associate, Office of Administration, Finance, and Public Awareness, 1989–present

Work, Harold, Secretary of the Academy, 1965–1968

Ziervogel, Stephanie, administrative secretary, Executive Office, 1982–1984

Ziff, Bradley, director, Office of Public Awareness, 1985–1986

Bibliography

Baxter, J. P. 1946. Scientists Against Time. Boston, Mass.: Little, Brown and Co.

Brown, A. 1965. Golden Gate. New York: Doubleday.

Cochrane, R. C. 1978. The National Academy of Sciences: The First Hundred Years, 1863-1963. Washington, D.C.: National Academy of Sciences.

Harriss, J. 1975. The Tallest Tower: Eiffel and the Belle Epoque. Boston, Mass.: Houghton Mifflin.

Jewett, F. B. 1948. The genesis of the National Research Council and Millikan's World War I work. Reviews of Modern Physics 2(1):1-12.

Lear, J. 1965. Research in America: Building the American dream Saturday Review of Literature (February 6):49-51.

National Academy of Engineering. 1976. The National Academy of Engineering: The first ten years. Washington, D.C.

Interviews

Richard Anthes
Jesse H. Ausubel
Stephen D. Bechtel, Jr.
Riley M. Chung
Jo Ann C. Clayton
John S. Coleman
S. Douglas Cornell
N. Bruce Hannay
John D. Holmfeld
J. Herbert Holloman
William G. Howard, Jr.
Raphael G. Kasper
Ralph Landau
Howard J. Lewis
Norman Metzger
Hugh H. Miller

James H. Mulligan, Jr.
Bruce S. Old
Courtland D. Perkins
John S. Perry
Kerstin B. Pollack
Frank Press
Simon Ramo
Robert C. Seamans, Jr.
Frederick Seitz
Chauncey Starr
H. Guyford Stever
Myron F. Uman
Eric A. Walker
John F. Welch, Jr.
Robert M. White

Name Index

Old, Bruce S., 40

Oppenheimer, J. Robert, 2

Peirce, Benjamin, 5

Perkins, Courtland D., 45, 50–54, 58, 60–62

Pickering, William H., 22

Pollack, Kerstin B., 35

Press, Frank, 56, 59, 60, 62, 66, 67, 87

Quinn, James Brian, 72

Reagan, Ronald, 69, 79, 85

Rechtin, Eberhardt, 42

Roosevelt, Franklin D., 13

Root, Elihu, 12

Rosenblith, Walter A., 58

Salmon, William C., 72

Schmitt, Roland W., 74, 76

Seamans, Robert C., Jr., 42–45, 47, 50

Seitz, Frederick, 11, 25–29, 37, 51

Shoupp, William E., 47

Sporn, Philip, 35, 52

Starr, Chauncey, 38

Steele, Lowell, 57

Stever, H. Guyford, 36, 58, 78, 79, 85, 86

Stratton, Julius A., 24–27, 29

Swasey, Ambrose, 23

Tolman, Richard, 13

Truman, Harry S, 20

Tschemy, George, 31

Van Allen, James A., 22

von Braun, Wernher, 22

von Karman, Theodore, 51

Walcott, Charles D., 10–12

Walker, Eric A., 4, 20, 24–27, 29, 31, 34, 35, 38, 40,
41, 52

Welch, John (Jack) F., Jr., 72, 78, 81

Welch, William H., 10, 11

Welles, Gideon, 5

White, Robert M., 59, 63, 66–71, 73, 77, 78, 80, 87,
92

Wilson, Henry, 5, 6

Wilson, Woodrow, 10, 11

Work, Harold K., 22–24, 29

Photography credits